Plan your life's g[illegible]
execute day by day and
achieve success in what you desire

CRUSHING YOUR NEXT 90 DAILY JOURNAL

TERENCE YOUNG, M.D.

Crushing Your Next 90 Daily Journal

ISBN: 978-1-7328535-3-9

Young Phoenix Enterprises, LLC

www.terenceyoungmd.com

www.docdeliversbooks.com

Danville, IL

Table of Contents

Crushing Your Next 90 Daily Journal

Going after the things that you desire can be a challenge for many people. Thus, I have tested and written this journal to assist you with your outcomes, as they have assisted me and many others before you.

Think of this journal as your personal accountability partner, guiding you along your journey, asking you the right questions so that you stay on track, remain motivated, and move steadily towards the outcomes that you desire!

With your commitment to this journal for the next 90 days, you will gradually develop the habits and mindset that will take you to the next level.

Even though it was designed to be a companion to my book, "Foundation Focus Freedom," it will serve you very well, building your **foundation** for success, **focusing** through your daily actions and goals, leading to the **freedom** to have the outcomes that you desire!

What outcomes do you desire to have in 90 days?

I congratulate you for taking the first step in purchasing this journal. Be proud of the commitment to take this step forward and start the journey of delivering the enhanced version of you!

As you turn the pages today and get started, you will discover a systematic approach towards creating and executing the outcomes that you desire. In 90 days, having accomplished your journey and feeling wonderful in every way, know that it was all due to the first steps that you took today.

Buckle up, stand strong, and let's get you started on your journey!

Understand your S.M.A.R.T. Outcomes

Understanding the S.M.A.R.T. Technique

The goal for this journal is to create, execute and achieve the outcomes that you desire within the next 90 days. Your outcomes will focus on three main categories, which I will describe shortly. First, it's important to understand the basic structure of a well-designed one.

Another way to think about your outcomes is by writing them down in a S.M.A.R.T. format. This is how I've been able to maintain my motivation and accomplish so much more than before. So, what makes a S.M.A.R.T. outcome smart?

It is Specific, Measurable, Achievable, Relevant, and Time-bound. Here is its mnemonic:

S – Specific

M - Measurable

A - Achievable

R - Relevant

T - Time-bound

Outcomes that are Specific, Measurable, Achievable, Relevant, and Time-bound are a systemized way of structuring them, providing you with a system that gives you a roadmap to success. It's the gift that keeps on giving.

Now, most people think or believe that you can just have a plan in your head and execute it effectively. But that's not very likely. Writing your plan down makes it real. It makes it a tangible thing. It acts as a step-by-step guide to achievement. With the correct plan, you can achieve in 90 days what takes most people an entire year. Or even longer.

How is this possible? That's what I'm about to show you. Let's talk about steps of planning out your S.M.A.R.T. outcomes, which will provide the template for setting up your 90-day path towards the enhanced version of you! First, you must break down the plan using the

S.M.A.R.T. technique. So, let's dig a little deeper into each of the components:

S is for... Specific

For an outcome to be "specific," it must be well defined and clear to anyone that reads it. But more importantly, it must be clear to you. Because you are the one who must do it! It should also serve a purpose to you. Why do you want to achieve your outcome and how will it benefit you and those around you?

M is for... Measurable

For an outcome to be measurable, it must have a specifically defined outcome. There must be a "finish line" so you are 100% sure when it is complete. By measurable, I mean their success or failure can be observed, assessed, and calculated. In short, make your outcomes quantifiable. An outcome of "losing 10 lbs. in 90 days" is far less ambiguous than "getting in shape." Measurable outcomes assist not only with achievement, but accountability as well.

A is for... Achievable

Make sure your outcome is achievable, meaning it is within the realm of possibility. Base it on your current situation and where you are at currently. It should stretch you but still be obtainable. Realistic outcomes are accomplishable ones. Setting impossible outcomes won't serve you in the long run. It's self-defeating and leads to a lot of negativity. Failing to "lose 10 lbs. in 90 days" is one thing. Failing to "grow 3 inches in 90 days" is another one entirely. But be careful you don't throw out a bold outcome just because others think it can't be done. The outcomes are about you first and foremost.

R is for... Relevant

Does the outcome align with your established core values? Will achieving it move you closer to your long-term visualization of the future version of yourself? Don't waste your time on an outcome that isn't helping you progress.

An outcome to "lose 10 lbs. in 90 days" doesn't make much sense to a chef experimenting with new recipes on the brink of opening her first restaurant. Non-relevant outcomes have the potential to set you up for failure. Not because you can't attain them. It's more along the lines of "who cares if we do?" If the outcomes don't align with your long-term vision that you have of yourself, it's probably not one that serves you best.

T is for... Timely

Can your outcome be tracked and completed by a specific date? Set hard dates to hit your outcomes and then take the physical step to mark them on the calendar. As you learn the upcoming 90-day plan for your outcomes, you will take the next step in your plans and proceed with breaking up your outcomes into smaller milestones or checkpoints. For the system I will teach you, these checkpoints will be goals that you strive for on a weekly and monthly basis. These mini targets and wins will keep you on the path to achievement.

So, there you have it. The S.M.A.R.T. outcome system!

When used properly, S.M.A.R.T. outcomes give you a solid plan of actionable steps to follow through. Think of all the goals you've had in your lifetime. Are you the person you dreamed of being? What prevented you from following through on any of your goals?

What would you do if you had the tools to accomplish any outcome, not in a few years, but in as little as a few months? Let's look at how

we might accomplish that with an example of having an outcome of being more physically fit and losing 20 pounds in 90 days.

So, the final outcome would be worded as:

“My goal is to lose 20 pounds in 90 days”.

Next, as we run it through the S.M.A.R.T. checklist, we have the following:

Specific – The outcome is clearly stated with a specific number in pounds and not as simply “lose weight”.

Measurable – This can be clearly measured because there is a target of 20 pounds.

Achievable – It’s realistic to say you can lose this amount in 90 days. A goal of losing 100 pounds, however, would not.

Relevant – The relevance would depend on a few factors. Is the outcome in line with your core values? For example, if your core values included fitness or health, this would be a relevant outcome.

Timely – This criterion is met because there is a well-defined time course for completion.

There you have it. A S.M.A.R.T. outcome will allow you to take action that is efficient, moving you closer towards the superior version of you. It sets you up for success and keeps you motivated along the way. And most importantly, because it’s trackable, you will see the results and milestones as you move forward.

Basic steps:

Step 1: Create your S.M.A.R.T. outcomes

Step 2: Establish your 28- and 56-day monthly expectations (MEs)

Step 3: Create your 1st months weekly previews

Step 4: Do your daily action sheets and nightly reflections

Step 5: Celebrate your success each step of the journey!

90-Day Outcome, Monthly Expectations and Weekly Review Sheets

The ***90-day outcome worksheet*** is where you will write down your S.M.A.R.T. outcomes.

First, let's clarify the difference between outcomes and goals:

Your **outcome** is the state or person that you strive to be, such as a more successful business person, or a closer connection with a higher being, spouse, or loved one. These are the 90-day targets that you will set.

Your **goals** are the waypoints along your journey to your outcomes. These are the daily, weekly, and monthly targets that you will set.

There are three outcome categories that you will focus upon:

Personal Self Outcomes

Social Self Outcomes

Financial Self Outcomes.

Your personal self includes the categories of *feelings, fitness, and fun.*

Outcomes that you can design within this category include examples such as:

Having an outcome to overcome your shyness by talking to two new people each week for the next four weeks.

Having an outcome to lose 20 pounds in the next 90 days.

Having an outcome to have a fun and exciting day trip once per month for the next three months.

Your external self includes the categories of *family, faith, and following.*

Some outcomes that you may have regarding this could be:

Having an outcome to have a family outing out of town once per month.

Having an outcome to spend 10 minutes every day for 30 days reading a spiritual body of work.

Having an outcome to share a positive message three times a week for the next month on Facebook live.

Your financial self includes the categories of *your internal financial worth, your external financial value, and your core financial happiness*. Some examples of these outcomes are:

Having an outcome to grow your business by 10% in the next 90 days.

Having an outcome to provide volunteer services in a homeless shelter for a total of eight hours in the next 30 days.

Having an outcome to design an office plan that will improve the morale of your fellow coworkers within the next 90 days.

Your 90-Day outcomes and the weekly and monthly goals:

To simplify the process, start with one outcome for the first 90-day cycle. If you feel you are up to the task, you can go for one out of each of the three categories. Also included within the journal is a section to record your "core values" and "My Why," your seven level deep statements that get to the core of why you wish to deliver an enhanced version of you! I feel it's important to document this, so you can open your journal and instantly see your why and values, especially important during the rough patches that you will encounter.

Your core values are the beliefs that you have about yourself, guiding your thoughts, beliefs, and actions towards the person who you wish to be. They are the elements guiding how you live your life day to day, for better or for worse.

On the sheet, you will write down two to four core values that resonate with you. If you need assistance selecting them, simply go to:

https://www.docdeliversbooks.com/free-ebook/ and you can access the worksheet titled "core values."

Your "why" statements reflect why you wish to achieve the goals and outcomes that you desire. As you go from statements one through seven, you continuously ask yourself why you desire what you do, digging deeper. In time, you will have a why so powerful, it will be your motivation when challenges or obstacles arise.

If you need assistance creating your seven level deep why statement, you can go to the worksheets at:

https://www.docdeliversbooks.com/free-ebook/ and simply access the worksheet titled "discover your why and be."

Finally, for this section, select your start and end dates. Technically, you have 91 days in the journal. For the technical people out there, your math will be on point!

This journal is a stand alone book. However, if you would like to know more about how I create, the importance of core values, and the why statements you can check out my main book, "Foundation Focus Freedom" by going to:

Bit.ly/DrYoungBooks

Your ***monthly expectations*** are your 90-day S.M.A.R.T. outcomes broken down into 28- and 56-day goals. On this sheet, your month one and two targets will be established, breaking down the 90-day outcome, which could be overwhelming, into smaller components. Do you know how to eat an elephant? One bite at a time!

In the ***monthly review sheets***, you will review if you did or didn't hit your monthly expectation goal(s) for your desired outcome(s).

If not, reflect upon the past month and determine why that was the case. This is also a checkpoint for seeing what you can do better for the upcoming month, even if you completed your expectations. Always look for the opportunity to grow. Finally, there is a section to record any reflections that you have for the month.

The ***weekly preview sheets*** are designed to further break down the monthly expectations into even more manageable goal(s) towards your overall outcome(s). Simply document the weekly goal that you commit to for that specific 90-day outcome. Take the time to stop and reflect upon your monthly expectation, making sure your weekly actions are moving you towards them and you are not simply filling your day with "stuff." Your outcome is to be "productive," not "busy."

With that being said, you will write down the "time vampires" that you will slay. These are the things like television, useless web browsing, social media channel engagement, which may be fun to do but suck the life and time out of your day.

Write down one that you will tackle or eliminate for the week. Finally, you have the space to write down any thoughts that you have for the upcoming week. Use this section as you best see fit!

Finally, let's break down the ***week in review sheets***. Here, you will document whether or not you achieved your personal, social, or financial goal(s) for the week. If so, wonderful. If not, wonderful! You have a great learning opportunity to see how to make this result even better, brainstorming on ways to minimize or eliminate the thing or things that caused you to fall short of the goal. Outside of this, if there are any other things that you feel you can improve upon for the week, write them down on the sheet. There is a spot just for this! Finally, you have the opportunity to reflect upon the week and share your thoughts with yourself and your worksheet!

Breakdown of your weekly time blocks

For each week, you are required to fulfill seven time blocks, which means you could commit to one block a day each day and complete the requirements that you need. Overall, these time blocks, when added together, will provide you with six hours towards your S.M.A.R.T. outcome.

Here are your required time blocks:

“The Time Efficient 25” or TE25

“The Magic 60” or M60

“The One Time 120” or OT120

“The Time Efficient 25” or TE25

The TE25 is based off the Pomodoro Technique which is focusing on working without distraction for 25 minutes, followed by a five-minute break to allow for you to mentally recharge.

The TE25 is the simplified version of the Pomodoro Technique because when expanded upon, it would involve cycles of 25 minutes of focused work, followed by five minutes of rest, after which the cycle repeats, up to two hours. This is how we will proceed with the OT120.

For your week, you will be required to schedule four blocks of TE25, placing and utilizing them as they best fit your schedule and outcome, respectively.

“The Magic 60” or M60

The M60 is simply two Pomodoro blocks, connected with a five-minute rest break in between, thus you would have a 25-minute block, followed by five minutes of rest, a second 25-minute block which again is followed by five minutes of rest.

For your week, you will be required to schedule two blocks of M60, placing and utilizing them as they best fit your schedule and outcome, respectively.

“The One Time 120” or OT120

The OT120 is simply four Pomodoro blocks, connected by five-minute rest breaks, thus every ½ hour during the two-hour time block, you are completing one 25-minute Pomodoro block followed by five minutes of rest.

For your week, you will be required to schedule one block of OT120, placing and utilizing it as it best fits your schedule and outcome, respectively.

Overall, these time blocks represent six hours of time that will be applied towards your S.M.A.R.T. outcome. So, you may ask, "Where do I put the time blocks at throughout my week?"

That my friend is totally up to you!

I have allowed you the flexibility to create your own schedule.

You could choose to have one time block a day for the seven days and be complete.

You could choose to do multiple time blocks, such as the OT120 on a weekend morning and a shorter TE25 later that day.

The key is to create a habit where you do a minimum of six hours of work a week, because after 90 days of doing it, it will become an automatic pattern for you.

Understand this:

The six hours of time blocks are a ***minimum*** because I, and many of my clients that I coach, understand the power of getting a massive amount of work done with undistracted and focused concentration. You could choose to add more time and to do this, simply add an extra TE25, M60 or OT120 to your schedule.

Let's make sure you truly understand the Pomodoro blocks. These are times with ZERO distractions.

Daily Actions and Nightly Reflections

Each day, in your personal journal or the manual that I created, and you have access to, you will mark down which time block(s) that you will complete for the day. If you have the sheet, simply circle the specific one that you commit to. These time blocks will correspond to the S.M.A.R.T. outcome that you desire, either: personal self outcomes, social self outcomes, or financial self outcomes.

As for now, I encourage you to start with ONE S.M.A.R.T. outcome for your first 90-day run. It's critical for you to get through the first 90 days without getting overwhelmed or frustrated because if that happens, your likelihood of quitting skyrockets and we don't want that! I say this because each S.M.A.R.T. outcome may potentially require extra time, so if you decide to tackle two of them, you're looking at 12 hours of time blocks during the week instead of six. If you do all three outcomes, now it's potentially 18 hours for the week.

Again, I will help you find the time that you need through the "time management" supplemental chapter which you can download for free by going to: https://www.docdeliversbooks.com/free-ebook/ and clicking on the link for the "time management" module.

Also, if you find that you can use more structure with your morning or evenings, you can access the same page and click on the link for my other supplemental chapter called "morning and evening rituals." Like the time management module, it is free as well.

Understand that there is no need to overwhelm yourself from day one. You potentially could do all three outcomes with just 12 hours of weekly time block commitments and you probably will be able to do so after developing the necessary habits, discipline, and efficiency that you gain from the first 90 days with just one S.MA.R.T. outcome.

After determining your time block for the day, you then will fill out the outcome (or simply task) that you desire for the day. Next, circle the one action that you will complete. If you are doing just one S.M.A.R.T. outcome, then this may be the only one you have on your sheet. If you have more than one S.M.A.R.T. outcome for the day, circling the one action that you commit to will remind you which one of the two (or three) are critical for the day.

After completing this is a very important step, which will frame your day in a positive way. Writing down your gratitude statements. Gratitude is essential in my life and has helped me achieve far more than I could have ever imagined! It doesn't have to be hard because you are just writing three things that you are currently grateful for. I write 10 every day, so three is easy peasy! This can be as simple as saying "I'm grateful for my family," or "I'm grateful for being alive today," or "I'm grateful for my job today."

When you are grateful for what you have, the doors of opportunity open for you because how would you ever expect to get more money, happiness, health, and wealth if you are not grateful for what you have now? Think about it.

Finally, for the daily action sheet, you will write a simple optimistic thought for the day. It could be your list of 3 – 5 core values. For example, I would write, "Today, I am a determined, disciplined and unstoppable man." It could be a power statement from your C.A.L.M.I.N.G. statements that you learned in the F.E.A.R. module of your second trimester from the main book "Foundation Focus Freedom." Here are the examples of those statements:

"I'm **C**onfident that I can…"

"I take **A**ction today to get closer to the outcomes tomorrow."

"**L**ife becomes more exciting as I grow out of my fear."

"**M**emories of success are within me."

"**I** can do anything for…"

"**N**ow is the time to act."

"**G**rowth is what I strive for, each and every day."

In your “Night Reflections,” we go back to the good ole Western days and reflect upon “The Good, The Bad, and The Ugly.”

Instead of ugly because it’s so negative, we will use O2E or your “opportunity to excel”

The good are the positives or victories that have been achieved during the day. Celebrate the wins whenever they come!

The bad are the things that didn’t go so well for you and that’s ok. Remember, these are learning opportunities that you will expand upon in the final section, your O2E.

Your O2E is your opportunity to further reflect and expand upon what didn’t work out so well and some possible solutions to minimizing or eliminating it in the future.

Next, you check off the time blocks that you completed today. Sounds simple but writing down and seeing this adds up, building the momentum of locking in a habit of doing daily time blocks.

At night, I love to reflect because it’s a quiet time for me and my mind is usually clear. Here, I brainstorm upon the potential actions that I desire for the next day.

There is the opportunity to write this down. Often, I skip writing down the actions on the night reflection and instantly document them on the next day’s daily action sheet. This way, I already have a head start on the next day. For me personally, my morning time before 11 AM is where I get most of my work done, so having the actions already planned out for the day is huge for me. Finally, I leave a section to record any additional thoughts that you may have. Feel free to use or not use this section as you best see fit.

Each day, locking in the one…

Since, you have seven time blocks that you will commit to each week, you most likely will have one per day. To help facilitate your success for the week, think of these blocks as the *absolute one that needs to be completed no matter what.* It is typically the most important task that you must complete and because of this, stress its importance and make the commitment to complete it. Will your S.M.A.R.T. outcomes totally collapse if you don't lock in and complete the one?

Absolutely not.

However, going through the 90 days, continually doing this will lock in a pattern, a habit that you don't want: complacency. Yes, there will be days when life overwhelms you and you are at the end of the day and your one is not complete. Suck it up and do it! You may think that one day is not doing to drastically change your life, but it definitely can. What if you failed to make that needed call to a client, the one who introduced you to someone who significantly brings your business to the next level? What if you decided to skip the gym today and on that day, your partner who was meant for you would have been on the treadmill besides you?

You just never know.

Am I excited *each and every day* I wake up at 4:45 AM to start my workouts? Hell no! Some days it sucks, and I think of every excuse not to do it, but I still push through it. Challenge yourself to grow to the next level, striving to get a little better each and every day. Believe me when I tell you this, when you complete the 90 days, those things that you previously thought as major obstacles will just be miniscule speedbumps along your journey.

So, as you progress through your day, understand that there is the one that must be completed. Within your "daily actions" sheet, you will mark or circle "the one" action that is the most important of the day. And as you complete the day and complete your nightly reflection, you will answer, simply yes or no, if you are

D.O.N.E. today or in other words:

Did **O**ne **N**ecessary **E**vent today.

If you say no, don't look upon it as a bad thing! It's simply a reflection of what didn't work today, providing you the opportunity to improve upon it. I grow and learn so much more from my failures than my successes that I treasure the opportunity to dissect out the issue and strive to set the plan that will minimize it from happening again.

Sample Pages…

With the following sample pages, I have given you an example of each type of sheet that you will fill in. The sheets are daily, nightly, weekly, monthly and the overall 90-day outcome sheet.

The samples are addressing THREE of the outcomes and if you are up for the challenge of doing three in a 90-day journey, go for it! If you are new to outcome setting and execution or have struggled with it before, I would encourage you to start slow and pick one or two outcomes for your 1st 90-day journey.

Once you have completed it and developed the habits necessary for the process, repeat it again with two or all three outcome categories. Your end goal is to have balance as you strive for you personal outcomes, social outcomes and financial outcomes simultaneously.

90-DAY OUTCOMES

Your Personal Self

By December 20th, 2019 I will have lost 30 pounds in body weight.

Your Social Self

By December 20th, 2019 I will have enhanced my relationship with my wife by having 10 or more two-hour dates

Your Financial Self

By December 20th, 2019 I will have raised an additional $2000 for my fundraising charity, Make a Wish Foundation.

My Core Values:

Determined	*Bold*
Enthusiastic	*Loving*

My Why:

1. *I desire my outcomes because I wish to be more happy and joyful.*
2. *I desire happiness and joy because I wish to live a life that excites me!*
3. *I desire excitement because I wish to share my success with others to inspire them.*
4. *I wish to inspire others and show that small shifts in their mindset can be powerful!*
5. *I wish to show that a powerful mindset can help you achieve all that you desire.*
6. *Achieving what you desire inspires others to do the same!*
7. *Inspiring others to also be inspiring will start making my community and my world a more exciting and happier place to be.*

Start date: __________ Finish date: __________

Month 1: MONTHLY EXPECTATIONS (MEs)

Your Personal Self ME: *Lose 10 pounds for 1st month exercising at least 15 times for 30 minutes and track my intake five days a week with daily calories under 2000.*

Your Social Self ME: *Have four at home dinner nights with my spouse, have a candlelight dinner and plan quiet time without TV, internet, or outside distractions.*

Your Financial Self ME: *Sign up for a charity and organize items around the house for a garage sale. Start my fund raising campaign on social media with four YouTube live videos.*

Month 2: MONTHLY EXPECTATIONS (MEs)

Your Personal Self ME: *Lose an additional 10 pounds, exercise 19 times for 30 minutes each adding four sessions of weight lifting.*

Your Social Self ME: *Plan 2 weekend day trips where we have a day trip for fun, at least 90 miles away from home.*

Your Financial Self ME: *Host my garage sale and have a set up an office raffle for donations with some remaining garage sale items.*

Month 3: MONTHLY EXPECTATIONS (MEs)

Your Personal Self ME: *Plan four weekend date nights outside the house, where we have dinner and movies without other family members.*

Your Social Self ME: *Lose my final 10 pounds, eating healthy six days a week, with daily caloric intake under 2000 calories.*

Your Financial Self ME: *Start a Go Fund Me account for any remaining money I need to raise and promote it in my community with flyers and door to door visits.*

MONTH 1 in Review

Personal MEs Achieved? If not, why?

No, lost 11 pounds and worked out 16 times but only did calorie intake under 2000 for 3 of the 4 weeks.

Social MEs Achieved? If not, why?

No, had only had 3 dinner nights, had unexpected job related work and cancelled one of the dinners.

Financial MEs Achieved? If not, why?

Yes, have a list of 102 items of things to sell at garage sale. And had 4 YouTube Live videos to support fundraising.

REVIEW YOUR <u>MONTHLY EXPECTATIONS</u> (MEs) TO MAKE SURE YOU ARE ON YOUR PATH FOR SUCCESS!!!

What is one thing I can do moving forward to better my month:

Focus more on my diet. Despite the weight loss I still had moments of overeating with calories going over 2000 for a day. Make sure my date nights are protected time and not to cancel in future.

Monthly Reflection:

I'm off to a great start but the biggest outcome is my date nights with my wife. I will go forward the next month committing to making all my monthly expectations. Keep up the strong work with the diet and I am excited that I am getting a lot of interest in my fundraiser. I should have made a Go Fund Me account from the start.

WEEK 1 Preview

Personal Outlook for Week: *Lose three pounds, eat healthy for five days and work out five times.*

Social Outlook for Week: *Have one date night with spouse and watch a movie.*

Financial Outlook for Week: *Go through the house and list at least 100 items I can have for my garage sale.*

REVIEW YOUR <u>MONTHLY EXPECTATIONS</u> (MEs) TO MAKE SURE YOU ARE ON YOUR PATH FOR SUCCESS!!!

What time vampire will I slay this week?

I will limit my Facebook time to 30 minutes per day

Thoughts for the Week:

I'm excited to get started with this first week. It may be challenging but I will keep pushing to get all my outlooks done!

WEEK 1 in Review

Personal Self for Week 1 Achieved? If not, why?

No, only lost two pounds and ate healthy for just three days.
Yes, I did work out five times this week.

Social Self for Week 1 Achieved? If not, why?

Yes, had a great date night and my spouse loved the movie!

Financial Self for Week 1 Achieved? If not, why?

Yes, starter list of 146 things on my list.

TOTAL TIME BLOCKS FOR WEEK:

5	1	1
TE25	M60	T120

REVIEW YOUR <u>MONTHLY EXPECTATIONS</u> (MEs) TO MAKE SURE YOU ARE ON YOUR PATH FOR SUCCESS!!!

What is one thing I can do moving forward to better my week?

Track my diet better. Start using a phone app like My Fitness Pal to keep better track of my diet.

Thoughts for the Week:

The list took A LOT more time than I realized but I'm glad I cut out TV on the weekend so that gave me the time needed to get it done for this week. I need to review some things on the list with the family and make sure it's ok to part with them for the garage sale. I got in all my time block except one of the TE25s.
This Sunday I will organize my weekly time blocks in advance, so I don't miss any of them.

Daily Actions: Week 1, Day 5

Personal Self Time	TE25	M60	OT120
Social Self Time	TE25	M60	OT120
Financial Self Time	TE25	M60	OT120

Personal Self Goal for Day: TIME *TE25*

Finish music playlist for date and have 15 songs.

Social Self Goal for Day: TIME *TE25*

30 minute workout, bike, and keep calories under 2000.

Financial Self Goal for Day: TIME *M60*

Look through kid's rooms today and see what we can sell.

Three Things I'm Grateful For:

1. *I'm grateful for my family.*
2. *I'm grateful I have a job to go to today.*
3. *I'm grateful for seeing the sun rise.*

Did you hydrate today? YES NO

Three Things You M.U.S.T. (Make You Strong Today) do:

1. *Hydrate during my workout and have fruit 30 minutes before start.*
2. *Listen to a motivational audio tape during me drive to work.*
3. *Read my "why" statement 3 times to remind me why I am doing my outcomes.*

NIGHT 5 REFLECTIONS:

The Good: *Got workout in, diet at 1869 calories today and swept kid's rooms for stuff on the list for garage sale.*

The Bad: *Only got six songs for list. More involved than I originally thought.*

Your O2E: *Look at maybe bigger time blocks for some projects.*

TIME BLOCKS COMPLETED TODAY:

2	1	0
TE25	M60	T120

Potential Actions for Tomorrow:

1. *Finish out playlist for date night and check out some movies we may see.*
2. *Cut out one hour of TV so I can focus more on my date night.*
3. *Start going through garage to see what to sell.*

Reflections of the Day:

I realized how much time I waste with small things like web browsing when I first wake up. I have felt more energy this week with my workouts and hydration so will keep that going! Try putting my phone downstairs in the kitchen so I'm not tempted to look at it first thing in the morning.

Are You D.O.N.E. Today? Yes  No

90-DAY OUTCOMES

We are ready to get started and you will begin by determining what your 90-day outcomes will look like. Remember, use the S.M.A.R.T. Technique to get them on point!

Your Personal Self

Your Social Self

Your Financial Self

Your Core Values:

Your Why:

1. ______________________________

____

2. ______________________________

____

3. ______________________________

____

4. ______________________________

____

5. ______________________________

____

6. ______________________________

____

7. ______________________________

Start Date: ______________ End Date: ______________

Month 1: MONTHLY EXPECTATIONS (MEs)

Your Personal Self ME: ______________________________

____

Your Social Self ME: ______________________________

____

Your Financial Self ME: ______________________________

____

Month 2: MONTHLY EXPECTATIONS (MEs)

Your Personal Self ME: ______________________________

____

Your Social Self ME: ______________________________

____

Your Financial Self ME: ______________________________

____

Month 3: MONTHLY EXPECTATIONS (MEs)

Your Personal Self ME: ______________________________

____

Your Social Self ME: ______________________________

____

Your Financial Self ME: ______________________________

____

WEEK 1 Preview

Personal Self Outlook for Week: ______________________________

____

____

Social Self Outlook for Week: ________________________________

____

____

Financial Self Outlook for Week: ______________________________

____

____

REVIEW YOUR MONTHLY EXPECTATIONS (MEs) TO MAKE SURE YOU ARE ON YOUR PATH FOR SUCCESS!!!

What time vampire will I slay this week?

____

Thoughts for the Week:

____

____

____

DAILY ACTIONS: Week 1, Day 1

Personal Self Time:	TE25	M60	OT120
Social Self Time:	TE25	M60	OT120
Financial Self Time:	TE25	M60	OT120

Personal Self Goal for Day: TIME: _______

____

____

Social Self Goal for Day: TIME: _______

____

____

Financial Self Goal for Day: TIME: _______

____

____

Three Things I'm Grateful For:

1. ____
2. ____
3. ____

Did you hydrate today? YES NO

Three Things You M.U.S.T. (Make You Strong Today) do:

1. ____

   ____
2. ____

   ____
3. ____

Night 1 Reflections:

The GOOD: ______

______

______

The BAD: ______

______

______

My O2E: ______

______

______

TIME BLOCKS COMPLETED TODAY:

TE25	M60	T120

Potential Actions for Tomorrow:

1. ______
2. ______
3. ______

Reflections of the Day:

______

______

Are You D.O.N.E. Today? Yes No

DAILY ACTIONS: Week 1, Day 2

Personal Self Time:	TE25	M60	OT120
Social Self Time:	TE25	M60	OT120
Financial Self Time:	TE25	M60	OT120

Personal Self Goal for Day: TIME: _______

____

____

Social Self Goal for Day: TIME: _______

____

____

Financial Self Goal for Day: TIME: _______

____

____

Three Things I'm Grateful For:

1. ____
2. ____
3. ____

Did you hydrate today? YES NO

Three Things You M.U.S.T. (Make You Strong Today) do:

1. ____

   ____
2. ____

   ____
3. ____

Night 2 Reflections:

The GOOD: ______________________________

____

____

The BAD: ______________________________

____

____

My O2E: ______________________________

____

____

TIME BLOCKS COMPLETED TODAY:

TE25	M60	T120

Potential Actions for Tomorrow:

1. ______________________________
2. ______________________________
3. ______________________________

Reflections of the Day:

____

____

Are You D.O.N.E. Today? Yes No

DAILY ACTIONS: Week 1, Day 3

Personal Self Time:	TE25	M60	OT120
Social Self Time:	TE25	M60	OT120
Financial Self Time:	TE25	M60	OT120

Personal Self Goal for Day: TIME: _______

Social Self Goal for Day: TIME: _______

Financial Self Goal for Day: TIME: _______

Three Things I'm Grateful For:

1. ____________________
2. ____________________
3. ____________________

Did you hydrate today? YES NO

Three Things You M.U.S.T. (Make You Strong Today) do:

1. ____________________
2. ____________________
3. ____________________

Night 3 Reflections:

The GOOD: ____

____

____

The BAD: ____

____

____

My O2E: ____

____

____

TIME BLOCKS COMPLETED TODAY:

TE25	M60	T120

Potential Actions for Tomorrow:

1. ____
2. ____
3. ____

Reflections of the Day:

____

____

Are You D.O.N.E. Today? Yes No

DAILY ACTIONS: Week 1, Day 4

Personal Self Time:	TE25	M60	OT120
Social Self Time:	TE25	M60	OT120
Financial Self Time:	TE25	M60	OT120

Personal Self Goal for Day: TIME: _______

____

____

Social Self Goal for Day: TIME: _______

____

____

Financial Self Goal for Day: TIME: _______

____

____

Three Things I'm Grateful For:

1. _______________
2. _______________
3. _______________

Did you hydrate today? YES NO

Three Things You M.U.S.T. (Make You Strong Today) do:

1. _______________

____

2. _______________

____

3. _______________

Night 4 Reflections:

The GOOD: ____

____

____

The BAD: ____

____

____

My O2E: ____

____

____

TIME BLOCKS COMPLETED TODAY:

TE25	M60	T120

Potential Actions for Tomorrow:

1. ____
2. ____
3. ____

Reflections of the Day:

____

____

Are You D.O.N.E. Today? Yes No

DAILY ACTIONS: Week 1, Day 5

Personal Self Time:	TE25	M60	OT120
Social Self Time:	TE25	M60	OT120
Financial Self Time:	TE25	M60	OT120

Personal Self Goal for Day: TIME: _______

Social Self Goal for Day: TIME: _______

Financial Self Goal for Day: TIME: _______

Three Things I'm Grateful For:

1.
2.
3.

Did you hydrate today? YES NO

Three Things You M.U.S.T. (Make You Strong Today) do:

1.
2.
3.

Night 5 Reflections:

The GOOD: ____

____

____

The BAD: ____

____

____

My O2E: ____

____

____

TIME BLOCKS COMPLETED TODAY:

TE25	M60	T120

Potential Actions for Tomorrow:

1. ____
2. ____
3. ____

Reflections of the Day:

____

____

Are You D.O.N.E. Today? Yes No

DAILY ACTIONS: Week 1, Day 6

Personal Self Time:	TE25	M60	OT120
Social Self Time:	TE25	M60	OT120
Financial Self Time:	TE25	M60	OT120

Personal Self Goal for Day: TIME: _______

Social Self Goal for Day: TIME: _______

Financial Self Goal for Day: TIME: _______

Three Things I'm Grateful For:

1.
2.
3.

Did you hydrate today? YES NO

Three Things You M.U.S.T. (Make You Strong Today) do:

1.
2.
3.

Night 6 Reflections:

The GOOD: ____________________

____

____

The BAD: ____________________

____

____

My O2E: ____________________

____

____

TIME BLOCKS COMPLETED TODAY:

TE25	M60	T120

Potential Actions for Tomorrow:

1. ____________________
2. ____________________
3. ____________________

Reflections of the Day:

____

____

Are You D.O.N.E. Today? Yes No

DAILY ACTIONS: Week 1, Day 7

Personal Self Time:	TE25	M60	OT120
Social Self Time:	TE25	M60	OT120
Financial Self Time:	TE25	M60	OT120

Personal Self Goal for Day: TIME: _______

____

____

Social Self Goal for Day: TIME: _______

____

____

Financial Self Goal for Day: TIME: _______

____

____

Three Things I'm Grateful For:

1. ____
2. ____
3. ____

Did you hydrate today? YES NO

Three Things You M.U.S.T. (Make You Strong Today) do:

1. ____

   ____

2. ____

   ____

3. ____

Night 7 Reflections:

The GOOD: ____

____

____

The BAD: ____

____

____

My O2E: ____

____

____

TIME BLOCKS COMPLETED TODAY:

TE25	M60	T120

Potential Actions for Tomorrow:

1. ____
2. ____
3. ____

Reflections of the Day:

____

____

Are You D.O.N.E. Today? Yes No

WEEK 1 in Review

Personal Self for Week 1 Achieved? If not, why?

Social Self for Week 1 Achieved? If not, why?

Financial Self for Week 1 Achieved? If not, why?

TOTAL TIME BLOCKS FOR WEEK:

TE25	M60	T120

REVIEW YOUR <u>MONTHLY EXPECTATIONS</u> (MEs) TO MAKE SURE YOU ARE ON YOUR PATH FOR SUCCESS!!!

What is one thing I can do moving forward to better my week?

Thoughts for the Week:

WEEK 2 Preview

Personal Self Outlook for Week: ______________________

____

____

Social Self Outlook for Week: ______________________

____

____

Financial Self Outlook for Week: ______________________

____

____

REVIEW YOUR MONTHLY EXPECTATIONS (MEs) TO MAKE SURE YOU ARE ON YOUR PATH FOR SUCCESS!!!

What time vampire will I slay this week?

____

Thoughts for the Week:

____

____

____

DAILY ACTIONS: Week 2, Day 8

Personal Self Time:	TE25	M60	OT120
Social Self Time:	TE25	M60	OT120
Financial Self Time:	TE25	M60	OT120

Personal Self Goal for Day: TIME: _______

____

____

Social Self Goal for Day: TIME: _______

____

____

Financial Self Goal for Day: TIME: _______

____

____

Three Things I'm Grateful For:

1. ____
2. ____
3. ____

Did you hydrate today? YES NO

Three Things You M.U.S.T. (Make You Strong Today) do:

1. ____

   ____
2. ____

   ____
3. ____

Night 8 Reflections:

The GOOD: ______________________________

____

____

The BAD: ______________________________

____

____

My O2E: ______________________________

____

____

TIME BLOCKS COMPLETED TODAY:

TE25	M60	T120

Potential Actions for Tomorrow:

1. ______________________________
2. ______________________________
3. ______________________________

Reflections of the Day:

____

____

Are You D.O.N.E. Today? Yes No

DAILY ACTIONS: Week 2, Day 9

Personal Self Time:	TE25	M60	OT120
Social Self Time:	TE25	M60	OT120
Financial Self Time:	TE25	M60	OT120

Personal Self Goal for Day: TIME: _______

Social Self Goal for Day: TIME: _______

Financial Self Goal for Day: TIME: _______

Three Things I'm Grateful For:

1.
2.
3.

Did you hydrate today? YES NO

Three Things You M.U.S.T. (Make You Strong Today) do:

1.
2.
3.

Night 9 Reflections:

The GOOD: ______________________________

____

____

The BAD: ______________________________

____

____

My O2E: ______________________________

____

____

TIME BLOCKS COMPLETED TODAY:

TE25	M60	T120

Potential Actions for Tomorrow:

1. ______________________________
2. ______________________________
3. ______________________________

Reflections of the Day:

____

____

Are You D.O.N.E. Today? Yes No

DAILY ACTIONS: Week 2, Day 10

Personal Self Time:	TE25	M60	OT120
Social Self Time:	TE25	M60	OT120
Financial Self Time:	TE25	M60	OT120

Personal Self Goal for Day: TIME: _______

Social Self Goal for Day: TIME: _______

Financial Self Goal for Day: TIME: _______

Three Things I'm Grateful For:

1. ____________
2. ____________
3. ____________

Did you hydrate today? YES NO

Three Things You M.U.S.T. (Make You Strong Today) do:

1. ____________
2. ____________
3. ____________

Night 10 Reflections:

The GOOD: ______________________________

____

____

The BAD: ______________________________

____

____

My O2E: ______________________________

____

____

TIME BLOCKS COMPLETED TODAY:

TE25	M60	T120

Potential Actions for Tomorrow:

1. ______________________________
2. ______________________________
3. ______________________________

Reflections of the Day:

____

____

Are You D.O.N.E. Today? Yes No

DAILY ACTIONS: Week 2, Day 11

Personal Self Time:	TE25	M60	OT120
Social Self Time:	TE25	M60	OT120
Financial Self Time:	TE25	M60	OT120

Personal Self Goal for Day: TIME: _______

___

___

Social Self Goal for Day: TIME: _______

___

___

Financial Self Goal for Day: TIME: _______

___

___

Three Things I'm Grateful For:

1. ___
2. ___
3. ___

Did you hydrate today? YES NO

Three Things You M.U.S.T. (Make You Strong Today) do:

1. ___

___

2. ___

___

3. ___

Night 11 Reflections:

The GOOD: ______________________________

____

____

The BAD: ______________________________

____

____

My O2E: ______________________________

____

____

TIME BLOCKS COMPLETED TODAY:

TE25	M60	T120

Potential Actions for Tomorrow:

1. ______________________________
2. ______________________________
3. ______________________________

Reflections of the Day:

____

____

Are You D.O.N.E. Today? Yes No

DAILY ACTIONS: Week 2, Day 12

Personal Self Time:	TE25	M60	OT120
Social Self Time:	TE25	M60	OT120
Financial Self Time:	TE25	M60	OT120

Personal Self Goal for Day: TIME: _______

____

____

Social Self Goal for Day: TIME: _______

____

____

Financial Self Goal for Day: TIME: _______

____

____

Three Things I'm Grateful For:

1. ____
2. ____
3. ____

Did you hydrate today? YES NO

Three Things You M.U.S.T. (Make You Strong Today) do:

1. ____

____

2. ____

____

3. ____

Night 12 Reflections:

The GOOD: ____

____

____

The BAD: ____

____

____

My O2E: ____

____

____

TIME BLOCKS COMPLETED TODAY:

TE25	M60	T120

Potential Actions for Tomorrow:

1. ____
2. ____
3. ____

Reflections of the Day:

____

____

Are You D.O.N.E. Today? Yes No

DAILY ACTIONS: Week 2, Day 13

Personal Self Time:	TE25	M60	OT120
Social Self Time:	TE25	M60	OT120
Financial Self Time:	TE25	M60	OT120

Personal Self Goal for Day: TIME: _______

____

____

Social Self Goal for Day: TIME: _______

____

____

Financial Self Goal for Day: TIME: _______

____

____

Three Things I'm Grateful For:

1. ____
2. ____
3. ____

Did you hydrate today? YES NO

Three Things You M.U.S.T. (Make You Strong Today) do:

1. ____

____

2. ____

____

3. ____

Night 13 Reflections:

The GOOD: ____

____

____

The BAD: ____

____

____

My O2E: ____

____

____

TIME BLOCKS COMPLETED TODAY:

TE25	M60	T120

Potential Actions for Tomorrow:

1. ____
2. ____
3. ____

Reflections of the Day:

____

____

Are You D.O.N.E. Today? Yes No

DAILY ACTIONS: Week 2, Day 14

Personal Self Time:	TE25	M60	OT120
Social Self Time:	TE25	M60	OT120
Financial Self Time:	TE25	M60	OT120

Personal Self Goal for Day: TIME: _______

___

___

Social Self Goal for Day: TIME: _______

___

___

Financial Self Goal for Day: TIME: _______

___

___

Three Things I'm Grateful For:

1. ___
2. ___
3. ___

Did you hydrate today? YES NO

Three Things You M.U.S.T. (Make You Strong Today) do:

1. ___

___

2. ___

___

3. ___

Night 14 Reflections:

The GOOD: ____________________

____

____

The BAD: ____________________

____

____

My O2E: ____________________

____

____

TIME BLOCKS COMPLETED TODAY:

TE25	M60	T120

Potential Actions for Tomorrow:

1. ____________________
2. ____________________
3. ____________________

Reflections of the Day:

____

____

Are You D.O.N.E. Today? Yes No

WEEK 2 in Review

Personal Self for Week 1 Achieved? If not, why?

Social Self for Week 1 Achieved? If not, why?

Financial Self for Week 1 Achieved? If not, why?

TOTAL TIME BLOCKS FOR WEEK:

TE25	M60	T120

REVIEW YOUR <u>MONTHLY EXPECTATIONS</u> (MEs) TO MAKE SURE YOU ARE ON YOUR PATH FOR SUCCESS!!!

What is one thing I can do moving forward to better my week?

Thoughts for the Week:

WEEK 3 Preview

Personal Self Outlook for Week: ______________________________

____

____

Social Self Outlook for Week: ______________________________

____

____

Financial Self Outlook for Week: ____________________________

____

____

REVIEW YOUR MONTHLY EXPECTATIONS (MEs) TO MAKE SURE YOU ARE ON YOUR PATH FOR SUCCESS!!!

What time vampire will I slay this week?

____

Thoughts for the Week:

____

____

____

DAILY ACTIONS: Week 3, Day 15

Personal Self Time:	TE25	M60	OT120
Social Self Time:	TE25	M60	OT120
Financial Self Time:	TE25	M60	OT120

Personal Self Goal for Day: TIME: _______

Social Self Goal for Day: TIME: _______

Financial Self Goal for Day: TIME: _______

Three Things I'm Grateful For:

1. ________
2. ________
3. ________

Did you hydrate today? YES NO

Three Things You M.U.S.T. (Make You Strong Today) do:

1. ________
2. ________
3. ________

Night 15 Reflections:

The GOOD: ____________________

____

____

The BAD: ____________________

____

____

My O2E: ____________________

____

____

TIME BLOCKS COMPLETED TODAY:

TE25	M60	T120

Potential Actions for Tomorrow:

1. ____________________
2. ____________________
3. ____________________

Reflections of the Day:

____

____

Are You D.O.N.E. Today? Yes No

DAILY ACTIONS: Week 3, Day 16

Personal Self Time:	TE25	M60	OT120
Social Self Time:	TE25	M60	OT120
Financial Self Time:	TE25	M60	OT120

Personal Self Goal for Day: TIME: _______

____

____

Social Self Goal for Day: TIME: _______

____

____

Financial Self Goal for Day: TIME: _______

____

____

Three Things I'm Grateful For:

1. ____
2. ____
3. ____

Did you hydrate today? YES NO

Three Things You M.U.S.T. (Make You Strong Today) do:

1. ____

   ____
2. ____

   ____
3. ____

Night 16 Reflections:

The GOOD: ______________________________

____

____

The BAD: ______________________________

____

____

My O2E: ______________________________

____

____

TIME BLOCKS COMPLETED TODAY:

TE25	M60	T120

Potential Actions for Tomorrow:

1. ______________________________
2. ______________________________
3. ______________________________

Reflections of the Day:

____

____

Are You D.O.N.E. Today? Yes No

DAILY ACTIONS: Week 3, Day 17

Personal Self Time:	TE25	M60	OT120
Social Self Time:	TE25	M60	OT120
Financial Self Time:	TE25	M60	OT120

Personal Self Goal for Day: TIME: _______

Social Self Goal for Day: TIME: _______

Financial Self Goal for Day: TIME: _______

Three Things I'm Grateful For:

1. ______
2. ______
3. ______

Did you hydrate today? YES NO

Three Things You M.U.S.T. (Make You Strong Today) do:

1. ______
2. ______
3. ______

Night 17 Reflections:

The GOOD: ____________________

____

____

The BAD: ____________________

____

____

My O2E: ____________________

____

____

TIME BLOCKS COMPLETED TODAY:

TE25	M60	T120

Potential Actions for Tomorrow:

1. ____________________
2. ____________________
3. ____________________

Reflections of the Day:

____

____

Are You D.O.N.E. Today? Yes No

DAILY ACTIONS: Week 3, Day 18

Personal Self Time:	TE25	M60	OT120
Social Self Time:	TE25	M60	OT120
Financial Self Time:	TE25	M60	OT120

Personal Self Goal for Day: TIME: ______

____

____

Social Self Goal for Day: TIME: ______

____

____

Financial Self Goal for Day: TIME: ______

____

____

Three Things I'm Grateful For:

1. ______________________________
2. ______________________________
3. ______________________________

Did you hydrate today? YES NO

Three Things You M.U.S.T. (Make You Strong Today) do:

1. ______________________________
____
2. ______________________________
____
3. ______________________________

Night 18 Reflections:

The GOOD: ____________________

____

____

The BAD: ____________________

____

____

My O2E: ____________________

____

____

TIME BLOCKS COMPLETED TODAY:

TE25	M60	T120

Potential Actions for Tomorrow:

1. ____________________
2. ____________________
3. ____________________

Reflections of the Day:

____

____

Are You D.O.N.E. Today? Yes No

DAILY ACTIONS: Week 3, Day 19

Personal Self Time:	TE25	M60	OT120
Social Self Time:	TE25	M60	OT120
Financial Self Time:	TE25	M60	OT120

Personal Self Goal for Day: TIME: _______

____

____

Social Self Goal for Day: TIME: _______

____

____

Financial Self Goal for Day: TIME: _______

____

____

Three Things I'm Grateful For:

1. ____
2. ____
3. ____

Did you hydrate today? YES NO

Three Things You M.U.S.T. (Make You Strong Today) do:

1. ____

____

2. ____

____

3. ____

Night 19 Reflections:

The GOOD: ____________________

____

____

The BAD: ____________________

____

____

My O2E: ____________________

____

____

TIME BLOCKS COMPLETED TODAY:

TE25	M60	T120

Potential Actions for Tomorrow:

1. ____________________
2. ____________________
3. ____________________

Reflections of the Day:

____

____

Are You D.O.N.E. Today? Yes No

DAILY ACTIONS: Week 3, Day 20

Personal Self Time:	TE25	M60	OT120
Social Self Time:	TE25	M60	OT120
Financial Self Time:	TE25	M60	OT120

Personal Self Goal for Day: TIME: ______

____

____

Social Self Goal for Day: TIME: ______

____

____

Financial Self Goal for Day: TIME: ______

____

____

Three Things I'm Grateful For:

1. ______________________________
2. ______________________________
3. ______________________________

Did you hydrate today? YES NO

Three Things You M.U.S.T. (Make You Strong Today) do:

1. ______________________________

____

2. ______________________________

____

3. ______________________________

Night 20 Reflections:

The GOOD: ____________________

____

____

The BAD: ____________________

____

____

My O2E: ____________________

____

____

TIME BLOCKS COMPLETED TODAY:

TE25	M60	T120

Potential Actions for Tomorrow:

1. ____________________
2. ____________________
3. ____________________

Reflections of the Day:

____

____

Are You D.O.N.E. Today? Yes No

DAILY ACTIONS: Week 3, Day 21

Personal Self Time:	TE25	M60	OT120
Social Self Time:	TE25	M60	OT120
Financial Self Time:	TE25	M60	OT120

Personal Self Goal for Day: TIME: _______

Social Self Goal for Day: TIME: _______

Financial Self Goal for Day: TIME: _______

Three Things I'm Grateful For:

1.
2.
3.

Did you hydrate today? YES NO

Three Things You M.U.S.T. (Make You Strong Today) do:

1.
2.
3.

Night 21 Reflections:

The GOOD: ____________________

____

____

The BAD: ____________________

____

____

My O2E: ____________________

____

____

TIME BLOCKS COMPLETED TODAY:

TE25	M60	T120

Potential Actions for Tomorrow:

1. ____________________
2. ____________________
3. ____________________

Reflections of the Day:

____

____

Are You D.O.N.E. Today? Yes No

WEEK 3 in Review

Personal Self for Week 1 Achieved? If not, why?

Social Self for Week 1 Achieved? If not, why?

Financial Self for Week 1 Achieved? If not, why?

TOTAL TIME BLOCKS FOR WEEK:

TE25	M60	T120

REVIEW YOUR MONTHLY EXPECTATIONS (MEs) TO MAKE SURE YOU ARE ON YOUR PATH FOR SUCCESS!!!

What is one thing I can do moving forward to better my week?

Thoughts for the Week:

WEEK 4 Preview

Personal Self Outlook for Week: ______________________________

____

____

Social Self Outlook for Week: ________________________________

____

____

Financial Self Outlook for Week: _____________________________

____

____

REVIEW YOUR MONTHLY EXPECTATIONS (MEs) TO MAKE SURE YOU ARE ON YOUR PATH FOR SUCCESS!!!

What time vampire will I slay this week?

____

Thoughts for the Week:

____

____

____

DAILY ACTIONS: Week 4, Day 22

Personal Self Time:	TE25	M60	OT120
Social Self Time:	TE25	M60	OT120
Financial Self Time:	TE25	M60	OT120

Personal Self Goal for Day: TIME: _______

Social Self Goal for Day: TIME: _______

Financial Self Goal for Day: TIME: _______

Three Things I'm Grateful For:

1.
2.
3.

Did you hydrate today? YES NO

Three Things You M.U.S.T. (Make You Strong Today) do:

1.
2.
3.

Night 22 Reflections:

The GOOD: ______________________________

____

____

The BAD: ______________________________

____

____

My O2E: ______________________________

____

____

TIME BLOCKS COMPLETED TODAY:

TE25	M60	T120

Potential Actions for Tomorrow:

1. ______________________________
2. ______________________________
3. ______________________________

Reflections of the Day:

____

____

Are You D.O.N.E. Today? Yes No

DAILY ACTIONS: Week 4, Day 23

Personal Self Time:	TE25	M60	OT120
Social Self Time:	TE25	M60	OT120
Financial Self Time:	TE25	M60	OT120

Personal Self Goal for Day: TIME: _______

____

____

Social Self Goal for Day: TIME: _______

____

____

Financial Self Goal for Day: TIME: _______

____

____

Three Things I'm Grateful For:

1. ____
2. ____
3. ____

Did you hydrate today? YES NO

Three Things You M.U.S.T. (Make You Strong Today) do:

1. ____

   ____
2. ____

   ____
3. ____

Night 23 Reflections:

The GOOD: ______________________________

____

____

The BAD: ______________________________

____

____

My O2E: ______________________________

____

____

TIME BLOCKS COMPLETED TODAY:

TE25	M60	T120

Potential Actions for Tomorrow:

1. ______________________________
2. ______________________________
3. ______________________________

Reflections of the Day:

____

____

Are You D.O.N.E. Today? Yes No

DAILY ACTIONS: Week 4, Day 24

Personal Self Time:	TE25	M60	OT120
Social Self Time:	TE25	M60	OT120
Financial Self Time:	TE25	M60	OT120

Personal Self Goal for Day: TIME: _______

____

____

Social Self Goal for Day: TIME: _______

____

____

Financial Self Goal for Day: TIME: _______

____

____

Three Things I'm Grateful For:

1. ____
2. ____
3. ____

Did you hydrate today? YES NO

Three Things You M.U.S.T. (Make You Strong Today) do:

1. ____

   ____
2. ____

   ____
3. ____

Night 24 Reflections:

The GOOD: ______________________________

____

____

The BAD: ______________________________

____

____

My O2E: ______________________________

____

____

TIME BLOCKS COMPLETED TODAY:

TE25	M60	T120

Potential Actions for Tomorrow:

1. ______________________________
2. ______________________________
3. ______________________________

Reflections of the Day:

____

____

Are You D.O.N.E. Today? Yes No

DAILY ACTIONS: Week 4, Day 25

Personal Self Time:	TE25	M60	OT120
Social Self Time:	TE25	M60	OT120
Financial Self Time:	TE25	M60	OT120

Personal Self Goal for Day: TIME: ______

____

____

Social Self Goal for Day: TIME: ______

____

____

Financial Self Goal for Day: TIME: ______

____

____

Three Things I'm Grateful For:

1. ______________________________
2. ______________________________
3. ______________________________

Did you hydrate today? YES NO

Three Things You M.U.S.T. (Make You Strong Today) do:

1. ______________________________

   ____
2. ______________________________

   ____
3. ______________________________

Night 25 Reflections:

The GOOD: ______________________________

The BAD: ______________________________

My O2E: ______________________________

TIME BLOCKS COMPLETED TODAY:

TE25	M60	T120

Potential Actions for Tomorrow:

1. ______________________________
2. ______________________________
3. ______________________________

Reflections of the Day:

____

Are You D.O.N.E. Today? Yes No

DAILY ACTIONS: Week 4, Day 26

Personal Self Time:	TE25	M60	OT120
Social Self Time:	TE25	M60	OT120
Financial Self Time:	TE25	M60	OT120

Personal Self Goal for Day: TIME: _______

Social Self Goal for Day: TIME: _______

Financial Self Goal for Day: TIME: _______

Three Things I'm Grateful For:

1. ______
2. ______
3. ______

Did you hydrate today? YES NO

Three Things You M.U.S.T. (Make You Strong Today) do:

1. ______
2. ______
3. ______

Night 26 Reflections:

The GOOD: ____________________

____

____

The BAD: ____________________

____

____

My O2E: ____________________

____

____

TIME BLOCKS COMPLETED TODAY:

TE25	M60	T120

Potential Actions for Tomorrow:

1. ____________________
2. ____________________
3. ____________________

Reflections of the Day:

____

____

Are You D.O.N.E. Today? Yes No

DAILY ACTIONS: Week 4, Day 27

Personal Self Time:	TE25	M60	OT120
Social Self Time:	TE25	M60	OT120
Financial Self Time:	TE25	M60	OT120

Personal Self Goal for Day: TIME: _______

____

____

Social Self Goal for Day: TIME: _______

____

____

Financial Self Goal for Day: TIME: _______

____

____

Three Things I'm Grateful For:

1. ____
2. ____
3. ____

Did you hydrate today? YES NO

Three Things You M.U.S.T. (Make You Strong Today) do:

1. ____

   ____
2. ____

   ____
3. ____

Night 27 Reflections:

The GOOD: ____________________

____

____

The BAD: ____________________

____

____

My O2E: ____________________

____

____

TIME BLOCKS COMPLETED TODAY:

TE25	M60	T120

Potential Actions for Tomorrow:

1. ____________________
2. ____________________
3. ____________________

Reflections of the Day:

____

____

Are You D.O.N.E. Today? Yes No

DAILY ACTIONS: Week 4, Day 28

Personal Self Time:	TE25	M60	OT120
Social Self Time:	TE25	M60	OT120
Financial Self Time:	TE25	M60	OT120

Personal Self Goal for Day: TIME: ______

____

____

Social Self Goal for Day: TIME: ______

____

____

Financial Self Goal for Day: TIME: ______

____

____

Three Things I'm Grateful For:

1. ______________________________
2. ______________________________
3. ______________________________

Did you hydrate today? YES NO

Three Things You M.U.S.T. (Make You Strong Today) do:

1. ______________________________

____

2. ______________________________

____

3. ______________________________

Night 28 Reflections:

The GOOD: ____________________

____

____

The BAD: ____________________

____

____

My O2E: ____________________

____

____

TIME BLOCKS COMPLETED TODAY:

TE25	M60	T120

Potential Actions for Tomorrow:

1. ____________________
2. ____________________
3. ____________________

Reflections of the Day:

____

____

Are You D.O.N.E. Today? Yes No

WEEK 4 in Review

Personal Self for Week 1 Achieved? If not, why?

Social Self for Week 1 Achieved? If not, why?

Financial Self for Week 1 Achieved? If not, why?

TOTAL TIME BLOCKS FOR WEEK:

TE25	M60	T120

REVIEW YOUR <u>MONTHLY EXPECTATIONS</u> (MEs) TO MAKE SURE YOU ARE ON YOUR PATH FOR SUCCESS!!!

What is one thing I can do moving forward to better my week?

Thoughts for the Week:

MONTH 1 in Review

Personal MEs Achieved? If not, why?

Social MEs Achieved? If not, why?

Financial MEs Achieved? If not, why?

REVIEW YOUR MONTHLY EXPECTATIONS (MEs) TO MAKE SURE YOU ARE ON YOUR PATH FOR SUCCESS!!!

What is one thing I can do moving forward to better my month:

Monthly Reflection:

Month 1 is complete!

Congratulations to your progress and continuing to strive for your outcomes.

Let's get set for the beginning of Month 2.

Remember to reflect upon your "Monthly Expectations Sheet"

and make sure you are on track for your Month 2 targets.

WEEK 5 Preview

Personal Self Outlook for Week: ______________________

____

____

Social Self Outlook for Week: ______________________

____

____

Financial Self Outlook for Week: ______________________

____

____

REVIEW YOUR MONTHLY EXPECTATIONS (MEs) TO MAKE SURE YOU ARE ON YOUR PATH FOR SUCCESS!!!

What time vampire will I slay this week?

____

Thoughts for the week:

____

____

____

DAILY ACTIONS: Week 5, Day 29

Personal Self Time:	TE25	M60	OT120
Social Self Time:	TE25	M60	OT120
Financial Self Time:	TE25	M60	OT120

Personal Self Goal for Day: TIME: _______

Social Self Goal for Day: TIME: _______

Financial Self Goal for Day: TIME: _______

Three Things I'm Grateful For:

1. ____________________
2. ____________________
3. ____________________

Did you hydrate today? YES NO

Three Things You M.U.S.T. (Make You Strong Today) do:

1. ____________________
2. ____________________
3. ____________________

Night 29 Reflections:

The GOOD: ____

____

____

The BAD: ____

____

____

My O2E: ____

____

____

TIME BLOCKS COMPLETED TODAY:

TE25	M60	T120

Potential Actions for Tomorrow:

1. ____
2. ____
3. ____

Reflections of the Day:

____

____

Are You D.O.N.E. Today? Yes No

DAILY ACTIONS: Week 5, Day 30

Personal Self Time:	TE25	M60	OT120
Social Self Time:	TE25	M60	OT120
Financial Self Time:	TE25	M60	OT120

Personal Self Goal for Day: TIME: ______

____

____

Social Self Goal for Day: TIME: ______

____

____

Financial Self Goal for Day: TIME: ______

____

____

Three Things I'm Grateful Today:

1. ______________________________
2. ______________________________
3. ______________________________

Did you hydrate today? YES NO

Three Things You M.U.S.T. (Make You Strong Today) do:

1. ______________________________

   ____
2. ______________________________

   ____
3. ______________________________

Night 30 Reflections:

The GOOD: ______________________________

____

____

The BAD: ______________________________

____

____

My O2E: ______________________________

____

____

TIME BLOCKS COMPLETED TODAY:

TE25	M60	T120

Potential Actions for Tomorrow:

1. ______________________________
2. ______________________________
3. ______________________________

Reflections of the Day:

____

____

Are You D.O.N.E. Today? Yes No

DAILY ACTIONS: Week 5, Day 31

Personal Self Time:	TE25	M60	OT120
Social Self Time:	TE25	M60	OT120
Financial Self Time:	TE25	M60	OT120

Personal Self Goal for Day: TIME: _______

____

____

Social Self Goal for Day: TIME: _______

____

____

Financial Self Goal for Day: TIME: _______

____

____

Three Things I'm Grateful For:

1. ____
2. ____
3. ____

Did you hydrate today? YES NO

Three Things You M.U.S.T. (Make You Strong Today) do:

1. ____

   ____
2. ____

   ____
3. ____

Night 31 Reflections:

The GOOD: ____________________

____

____

The BAD: ____________________

____

____

My O2E: ____________________

____

____

TIME BLOCKS COMPLETED TODAY:

TE25	M60	T120

Potential Actions for Tomorrow:

1. ____________________
2. ____________________
3. ____________________

Reflections of the Day:

____

____

Are You D.O.N.E. Today? Yes No

DAILY ACTIONS: Week 5, Day 32

Personal Self Time:	TE25	M60	OT120
Social Self Time:	TE25	M60	OT120
Financial Self Time:	TE25	M60	OT120

Personal Self Goal for Day: TIME: _______

____

____

Social Self Goal for Day: TIME: _______

____

____

Financial Self Goal for Day: TIME: _______

____

____

Three Things I'm Grateful For:

1. ______________________________
2. ______________________________
3. ______________________________

Did you hydrate today? YES NO

Three Things You M.U.S.T. (Make You Strong Today) do:

1. ______________________________
   ____
2. ______________________________
   ____
3. ______________________________

Night 32 Reflections:

The GOOD: ______________________________

____

____

The BAD: ______________________________

____

____

My O2E: ______________________________

____

____

TIME BLOCKS COMPLETED TODAY:

TE25	M60	T120

Potential Actions for Tomorrow:

1. ______________________________
2. ______________________________
3. ______________________________

Reflections of the Day:

____

____

Are You D.O.N.E. Today? Yes No

DAILY ACTIONS: Week 5, Day 33

Personal Self Time:	TE25	M60	OT120
Social Self Time:	TE25	M60	OT120
Financial Self Time:	TE25	M60	OT120

Personal Self Goal for Day: TIME: _______

____

____

Social Self Goal for Day: TIME: _______

____

____

Financial Self Goal for Day: TIME: _______

____

____

Three Things I'm Grateful For:

1. _______________
2. _______________
3. _______________

Did you hydrate today? YES NO

Three Things You M.U.S.T. (Make You Strong Today) do:

1. _______________

____

2. _______________

____

3. _______________

Night 33 Reflections:

The GOOD: ______________________________

____

____

The BAD: ______________________________

____

____

My O2E: ______________________________

____

____

TIME BLOCKS COMPLETED TODAY:

TE25	M60	T120

Potential Actions for Tomorrow:

1. ______________________________
2. ______________________________
3. ______________________________

Reflections of the Day:

____

____

Are You D.O.N.E. Today? Yes No

DAILY ACTIONS: Week 5, Day 34

Personal Self Time:	TE25	M60	OT120
Social Self Time:	TE25	M60	OT120
Financial Self Time:	TE25	M60	OT120

Personal Self Goal for Day: TIME: _______

___

___

Social Self Goal for Day: TIME: _______

___

___

Financial Self Goal for Day: TIME: _______

___

___

Three Things I'm Grateful For:

1. ___
2. ___
3. ___

Did you hydrate today? YES NO

Three Things You M.U.S.T. (Make You Strong Today) do:

1. ___

   ___
2. ___

   ___
3. ___

Night 34 Reflections:

The GOOD: ____________________

____

____

The BAD: ____________________

____

____

My O2E: ____________________

____

____

TIME BLOCKS COMPLETED TODAY:

TE25	M60	T120

Potential Actions for Tomorrow:

1. ____________________
2. ____________________
3. ____________________

Reflections of the Day:

____

____

Are You D.O.N.E. Today? Yes No

DAILY ACTIONS: Week 5, Day 35

Personal Self Time:	TE25	M60	OT120
Social Self Time:	TE25	M60	OT120
Financial Self Time:	TE25	M60	OT120

Personal Self Goal for Day: TIME: _______

Social Self Goal for Day: TIME: _______

Financial Self Goal for Day: TIME: _______

Three Things I'm Grateful For:

1.
2.
3.

Did you hydrate today? YES NO

Three Things You M.U.S.T. (Make You Strong Today) do:

1.
2.
3.

Night 35 Reflections:

The GOOD: ______________________________

____

____

The BAD: ______________________________

____

____

My O2E: ______________________________

____

____

TIME BLOCKS COMPLETED TODAY:

TE25	M60	T120

Potential Actions for Tomorrow:

1. ______________________________
2. ______________________________
3. ______________________________

Reflections of the Day:

____

____

Are You D.O.N.E. Today? Yes No

WEEK 5 in Review

Personal Self for Week 1 Achieved? If not, why?

Social Self for Week 1 Achieved? If not, why?

Financial Self for Week 1 Achieved? If not, why?

TOTAL TIME BLOCKS FOR WEEK:

TE25	M60	T120

REVIEW YOUR MONTHLY EXPECTATIONS (MEs) TO MAKE SURE YOU ARE ON YOUR PATH FOR SUCCESS!!!

What is one thing I can do moving forward to better my week?

Thoughts for the week:

WEEK 6 Preview

Personal Self Outlook for Week: ______________________________

____

____

Social Self Outlook for Week: ______________________________

____

____

Financial Self Outlook for Week: ______________________________

____

____

REVIEW YOUR MONTHLY EXPECTATIONS (MEs) TO MAKE SURE YOU ARE ON YOUR PATH FOR SUCCESS!!!

What time vampire will I slay this week?

____

Thoughts for the week:

____

____

____

DAILY ACTIONS: Week 6, Day 36

Personal Self Time:	TE25	M60	OT120
Social Self Time:	TE25	M60	OT120
Financial Self Time:	TE25	M60	OT120

Personal Self Goal for Day: TIME: _______

Social Self Goal for Day: TIME: _______

Financial Self Goal for Day: TIME: _______

Three Things I'm Grateful For:

1.
2.
3.

Did you hydrate today? YES NO

Three Things You M.U.S.T. (Make You Strong Today) do:

1.
2.
3.

Night 36 Reflections:

The GOOD: ____________________

____

____

The BAD: ____________________

____

____

My O2E: ____________________

____

____

TIME BLOCKS COMPLETED TODAY:

TE25	M60	T120

Potential Actions for Tomorrow:

1. ____________________
2. ____________________
3. ____________________

Reflections of the Day:

____

____

Are You D.O.N.E. Today? Yes No

DAILY ACTIONS: Week 6, Day 37

Personal Self Time:	TE25	M60	OT120
Social Self Time:	TE25	M60	OT120
Financial Self Time:	TE25	M60	OT120

Personal Self Goal for Day: TIME: _______

____

____

Social Self Goal for Day: TIME: _______

____

____

Financial Self Goal for Day: TIME: _______

____

____

Three Things I'm Grateful For:

1. ____
2. ____
3. ____

Did you hydrate today? YES NO

Three Things You M.U.S.T. (Make You Strong Today) do:

1. ____

____

2. ____

____

3. ____

Night 37 Reflections:

The GOOD: ____

____

____

The BAD: ____

____

____

My O2E: ____

____

____

TIME BLOCKS COMPLETED TODAY:

TE25	M60	T120

Potential Actions for Tomorrow:

1. ____
2. ____
3. ____

Reflections of the Day:

____

____

Are You D.O.N.E. Today? Yes No

DAILY ACTIONS: Week 6, Day 38

Personal Self Time:	TE25	M60	OT120
Social Self Time:	TE25	M60	OT120
Financial Self Time:	TE25	M60	OT120

Personal Self Goal for Day: TIME: _______

____

____

Social Self Goal for Day: TIME: _______

____

____

Financial Self Goal for Day: TIME: _______

____

____

Three Things I'm Grateful For:

1. ____
2. ____
3. ____

Did you hydrate today? YES NO

Three Things You M.U.S.T. (Make You Strong Today) do:

1. ____

   ____
2. ____

   ____
3. ____

Night 38 Reflections:

The GOOD: ______________________________

____

____

The BAD: ______________________________

____

____

My O2E: ______________________________

____

____

TIME BLOCKS COMPLETED TODAY:

TE25	M60	T120

Potential Actions for Tomorrow:

1. ______________________________
2. ______________________________
3. ______________________________

Reflections of the Day:

____

____

Are You D.O.N.E. Today? Yes No

DAILY ACTIONS: Week 6, Day 39

Personal Self Time:	TE25	M60	OT120
Social Self Time:	TE25	M60	OT120
Financial Self Time:	TE25	M60	OT120

Personal Self Goal for Day: TIME: _______

Social Self Goal for Day: TIME: _______

Financial Self Goal for Day: TIME: _______

Three Things I'm Grateful For:

1. ____________________
2. ____________________
3. ____________________

Did you hydrate today? YES NO

Three Things You M.U.S.T. (Make You Strong Today) do:

1. ____________________
2. ____________________
3. ____________________

Night 39 Reflections:

The GOOD: ____________________

____

____

The BAD: ____________________

____

____

My O2E: ____________________

____

____

TIME BLOCKS COMPLETED TODAY:

TE25	M60	T120

Potential Actions for Tomorrow:

1. ____________________
2. ____________________
3. ____________________

Reflections of the Day:

____

____

Are You D.O.N.E. Today? Yes No

DAILY ACTIONS: Week 6, Day 40

Personal Self Time:	TE25	M60	OT120
Social Self Time:	TE25	M60	OT120
Financial Self Time:	TE25	M60	OT120

Personal Self Goal for Day: TIME: _______

Social Self Goal for Day: TIME: _______

Financial Self Goal for Day: TIME: _______

Three Things I'm Grateful For:

1.
2.
3.

Did you hydrate today? YES NO

Three Things You M.U.S.T. (Make You Strong Today) do:

1.
2.
3.

Night 40 Reflections:

The GOOD: ______________________________

____

____

The BAD: ______________________________

____

____

My O2E: ______________________________

____

____

TIME BLOCKS COMPLETED TODAY:

TE25	M60	T120

Potential Actions for Tomorrow:

1. ______________________________
2. ______________________________
3. ______________________________

Reflections of the Day:

____

____

Are You D.O.N.E. Today? Yes No

DAILY ACTIONS: Week 6, Day 41

Personal Self Time:	TE25	M60	OT120
Social Self Time:	TE25	M60	OT120
Financial Self Time:	TE25	M60	OT120

Personal Self Goal for Day: TIME: ______

____

____

Social Self Goal for Day: TIME: ______

____

____

Financial Self Goal for Day: TIME: ______

____

____

Three Things I'm Grateful For:

1. ______________________________
2. ______________________________
3. ______________________________

Did you hydrate today? YES NO

Three Things You M.U.S.T. (Make You Strong Today) do:

1. ______________________________

   ____
2. ______________________________

   ____
3. ______________________________

Night 41 Reflections:

The GOOD: ____

____

____

The BAD: ____

____

____

My O2E: ____

____

____

TIME BLOCKS COMPLETED TODAY:

TE25	M60	T120

Potential Actions for Tomorrow:

1. ____
2. ____
3. ____

Reflections of the Day:

____

____

Are You D.O.N.E. Today? Yes No

DAILY ACTIONS: Week 6, Day 42

Personal Self Time:	TE25	M60	OT120
Social Self Time:	TE25	M60	OT120
Financial Self Time:	TE25	M60	OT120

Personal Self Goal for Day: TIME: ______

Social Self Goal for Day: TIME: ______

Financial Self Goal for Day: TIME: ______

Three Things I'm Grateful For:

1. ______
2. ______
3. ______

Did you hydrate today? YES NO

Three Things You M.U.S.T. (Make You Strong Today) do:

1. ______
2. ______
3. ______

Night 42 Reflections:

The GOOD: ______________________________

____

____

The BAD: ______________________________

____

____

My O2E: ______________________________

____

____

TIME BLOCKS COMPLETED TODAY:

TE25	M60	T120

Potential Actions for Tomorrow:

1. ______________________________
2. ______________________________
3. ______________________________

Reflections of the Day:

____

____

Are You D.O.N.E. Today? Yes No

WEEK 6 in Review

Personal Self for Week 1 Achieved? If not, why?

Social Self for Week 1 Achieved? If not, why?

Financial Self for Week 1 Achieved? If not, why?

TOTAL TIME BLOCKS FOR WEEK:

TE25	M60	T120

REVIEW YOUR <u>MONTHLY EXPECTATIONS</u> (MEs) TO MAKE SURE YOU ARE ON YOUR PATH FOR SUCCESS!!!

What is one thing I can do moving forward to better my week?

Thoughts for the Week:

WEEK 7 Preview

Personal Self Outlook for Week: ______________________________

____

____

Social Self Outlook for Week: ______________________________

____

____

Financial Self Outlook for Week: ______________________________

____

____

REVIEW YOUR MONTHLY EXPECTATIONS (MEs) TO MAKE SURE YOU ARE ON YOUR PATH FOR SUCCESS!!!

What time vampire will I slay this week?

____

Thoughts for the week:

____

____

____

DAILY ACTIONS: Week 7, Day 43

Personal Self Time:	TE25	M60	OT120
Social Self Time:	TE25	M60	OT120
Financial Self Time:	TE25	M60	OT120

Personal Self Goal for Day: TIME: _______

____

____

Social Self Goal for Day: TIME: _______

____

____

Financial Self Goal for Day: TIME: _______

____

____

Three Things I'm Grateful For:

1. ____
2. ____
3. ____

Did you hydrate today? YES NO

Three Things You M.U.S.T. (Make You Strong Today) do:

1. ____

   ____
2. ____

   ____
3. ____

Night 43 Reflections:

The GOOD: ______________________________

____

____

The BAD: ______________________________

____

____

My O2E: ______________________________

____

____

TIME BLOCKS COMPLETED TODAY:

TE25	M60	T120

Potential Actions for Tomorrow:

1. ______________________________
2. ______________________________
3. ______________________________

Reflections of the Day:

____

____

Are You D.O.N.E. Today? Yes No

DAILY ACTIONS: Week 7, Day 44

Personal Self Time:	TE25	M60	OT120
Social Self Time:	TE25	M60	OT120
Financial Self Time:	TE25	M60	OT120

Personal Self Goal for Day: TIME: _______

____

____

Social Self Goal for Day: TIME: _______

____

____

Financial Self Goal for Day: TIME: _______

____

____

Three Things I'm Grateful For:

1. ____
2. ____
3. ____

Did you hydrate today? YES NO

Three Things You M.U.S.T. (Make You Strong Today) do:

1. ____

   ____
2. ____

   ____
3. ____

Night 44 Reflections:

The GOOD: ______________________________

____

____

The BAD: ______________________________

____

____

My O2E: ______________________________

____

____

TIME BLOCKS COMPLETED TODAY:

TE25	M60	T120

Potential Actions for Tomorrow:

1. ______________________________
2. ______________________________
3. ______________________________

Reflections of the Day:

____

____

Are You D.O.N.E. Today? Yes No

DAILY ACTIONS: Week 7, Day 45

Personal Self Time:	TE25	M60	OT120
Social Self Time:	TE25	M60	OT120
Financial Self Time:	TE25	M60	OT120

Personal Self Goal for Day: TIME: _______

____

____

Social Self Goal for Day: TIME: _______

____

____

Financial Self Goal for Day: TIME: _______

____

____

Three Things I'm Grateful For:

1. ______________________________________
2. ______________________________________
3. ______________________________________

Did you hydrate today? YES NO

Three Things You M.U.S.T. (Make You Strong Today) do:

1. ______________________________________

   ____
2. ______________________________________

   ____
3. ______________________________________

Night 45 Reflections:

The GOOD: ______________________________

____

____

The BAD: ______________________________

____

____

My O2E: ______________________________

____

____

TIME BLOCKS COMPLETED TODAY:

TE25	M60	T120

Potential Actions for Tomorrow:

1. ______________________________
2. ______________________________
3. ______________________________

Reflections of the Day:

____

____

Are You D.O.N.E. Today? Yes No

DAILY ACTIONS: Week 7, Day 46

Personal Self Time:	TE25	M60	OT120
Social Self Time:	TE25	M60	OT120
Financial Self Time:	TE25	M60	OT120

Personal Self Goal for Day: TIME: _______

____

____

Social Self Goal for Day: TIME: _______

____

____

Financial Self Goal for Day: TIME: _______

____

____

Three Things I'm Grateful For:

1. ____
2. ____
3. ____

Did you hydrate today? YES NO

Three Things You M.U.S.T. (Make You Strong Today) do:

1. ____

   ____
2. ____

   ____
3. ____

Night 46 Reflections:

The GOOD: ____________________

____

____

The BAD: ____________________

____

____

My O2E: ____________________

____

____

TIME BLOCKS COMPLETED TODAY:

TE25	M60	T120

Potential Actions for Tomorrow:

1. ____________________
2. ____________________
3. ____________________

Reflections of the Day:

____

____

Are You D.O.N.E. Today? Yes No

DAILY ACTIONS: Week 7, Day 47

Personal Self Time:	TE25	M60	OT120
Social Self Time:	TE25	M60	OT120
Financial Self Time:	TE25	M60	OT120

Personal Self Goal for Day: TIME: _______

____

____

Social Self Goal for Day: TIME: _______

____

____

Financial Self Goal for Day: TIME: _______

____

____

Three Things I'm Grateful For:

1. _______________
2. _______________
3. _______________

Did you hydrate today? YES NO

Three Things You M.U.S.T. (Make You Strong Today) do:

1. _______________
____
2. _______________
____
3. _______________

Night 47 Reflections:

The GOOD: ____________________

____

____

The BAD: ____________________

____

____

My O2E: ____________________

____

____

TIME BLOCKS COMPLETED TODAY:

TE25	M60	T120

Potential Actions for Tomorrow:

1. ____________________
2. ____________________
3. ____________________

Reflections of the Day:

____

____

Are You D.O.N.E. Today? Yes No

DAILY ACTIONS: Week 7, Day 48

Personal Self Time:	TE25	M60	OT120
Social Self Time:	TE25	M60	OT120
Financial Self Time:	TE25	M60	OT120

Personal Self Goal for Day: TIME: _______

____

____

Social Self Goal for Day: TIME: _______

____

____

Financial Self Goal for Day: TIME: _______

____

____

Three Things I'm Grateful For:

1. ____
2. ____
3. ____

Did you hydrate today? YES NO

Three Things You M.U.S.T. (Make You Strong Today) do:

1. ____

   ____
2. ____

   ____
3. ____

Night 48 Reflections:

The GOOD: ____________________

____

____

The BAD: ____________________

____

____

My O2E: ____________________

____

____

TIME BLOCKS COMPLETED TODAY:

TE25	M60	T120

Potential Actions for Tomorrow:

1. ____________________
2. ____________________
3. ____________________

Reflections of the Day:

____

____

Are You D.O.N.E. Today? Yes No

DAILY ACTIONS: Week 7, Day 49

Personal Self Time:	TE25	M60	OT120
Social Self Time:	TE25	M60	OT120
Financial Self Time:	TE25	M60	OT120

Personal Self Goal for Day: TIME: _______

Social Self Goal for Day: TIME: _______

Financial Self Goal for Day: TIME: _______

Three Things I'm Grateful For:

1. ______
2. ______
3. ______

Did you hydrate today? YES NO

Three Things You M.U.S.T. (Make You Strong Today) do:

1. ______
2. ______
3. ______

Night 49 Reflections:

The GOOD: ____

____

____

The BAD: ____

____

____

My O2E: ____

____

____

TIME BLOCKS COMPLETED TODAY:

TE25	M60	T120

Potential Actions for Tomorrow:

1. ____
2. ____
3. ____

Reflections of the Day:

____

____

Are You D.O.N.E. Today? Yes No

WEEK 7 in Review

Personal Self for Week 1 Achieved? If not, why?

Social Self for Week 1 Achieved? If not, why?

Financial Self for Week 1 Achieved? If not, why?

TOTAL TIME BLOCKS FOR WEEK:

TE25	M60	T120

REVIEW YOUR MONTHLY EXPECTATIONS (MEs) TO MAKE SURE YOU ARE ON YOUR PATH FOR SUCCESS!!!

What is one thing I can do moving forward to better my week?

Thoughts for the Week:

WEEK 8 Preview

Personal Self Outlook for Week: ____________________________

____

____

Social Self Outlook for Week: ______________________________

____

____

Financial Self Outlook for Week: ___________________________

____

____

REVIEW YOUR MONTHLY EXPECTATIONS (MEs) TO MAKE SURE YOU ARE ON YOUR PATH FOR SUCCESS!!!

What time vampire will I slay this week?

____

Thoughts for the Week:

____

____

____

DAILY ACTIONS: Week 8, Day 50

Personal Self Time:	TE25	M60	OT120
Social Self Time:	TE25	M60	OT120
Financial Self Time:	TE25	M60	OT120

Personal Self Goal for Day: TIME: ______

____

____

Social Self Goal for Day: TIME: ______

____

____

Financial Self Goal for Day: TIME: ______

____

____

Three Things I'm Grateful For:

1. ____________________
2. ____________________
3. ____________________

Did you hydrate today? YES NO

Three Things You M.U.S.T. (Make You Strong Today) do:

1. ____________________

   ____
2. ____________________

   ____
3. ____________________

Night 50 Reflections:

The GOOD: ____________________

____

____

The BAD: ____________________

____

____

My O2E: ____________________

____

____

TIME BLOCKS COMPLETED TODAY:

TE25	M60	T120

Potential Actions for Tomorrow:

1. ____________________
2. ____________________
3. ____________________

Reflections of the Day:

____

____

Are You D.O.N.E. Today? Yes No

DAILY ACTIONS: Week 8, Day 51

Personal Self Time:	TE25	M60	OT120
Social Self Time:	TE25	M60	OT120
Financial Self Time:	TE25	M60	OT120

Personal Self Goal for Day: TIME: _______

Social Self Goal for Day: TIME: _______

Financial Self Goal for Day: TIME: _______

Three Things I'm Grateful For:

1. ________
2. ________
3. ________

Did you hydrate today? YES NO

Three Things You M.U.S.T. (Make You Strong Today) do:

1. ________
2. ________
3. ________

Night 51 Reflections:

The GOOD: ______________________________

____

____

The BAD: ______________________________

____

____

My O2E: ______________________________

____

____

TIME BLOCKS COMPLETED TODAY:

TE25	M60	T120

Potential Actions for Tomorrow:

1. ______________________________
2. ______________________________
3. ______________________________

Reflections of the Day:

____

____

Are You D.O.N.E. Today? Yes No

DAILY ACTIONS: Week 8, Day 52

Personal Self Time:	TE25	M60	OT120
Social Self Time:	TE25	M60	OT120
Financial Self Time:	TE25	M60	OT120

Personal Self Goal for Day: TIME: _______

____

____

Social Self Goal for Day: TIME: _______

____

____

Financial Self Goal for Day: TIME: _______

____

____

Three Things I'm Grateful For:

1. ____
2. ____
3. ____

Did you hydrate today? YES NO

Three Things You M.U.S.T. (Make You Strong Today) do:

1. ____

____

2. ____

____

3. ____

Night 52 Reflections:

The GOOD: ____________________

____

____

The BAD: ____________________

____

____

My O2E: ____________________

____

____

TIME BLOCKS COMPLETED TODAY:

TE25	M60	T120

Potential Actions for Tomorrow:

1. ____________________
2. ____________________
3. ____________________

Reflections of the Day:

____

____

Are You D.O.N.E. Today? Yes No

DAILY ACTIONS: Week 8, Day 53

Personal Self Time:	TE25	M60	OT120
Social Self Time:	TE25	M60	OT120
Financial Self Time:	TE25	M60	OT120

Personal Self Goal for Day: TIME: _______

Social Self Goal for Day: TIME: _______

Financial Self Goal for Day: TIME: _______

Three Things I'm Grateful For:

1.
2.
3.

Did you hydrate today? YES NO

Three Things You M.U.S.T. (Make You Strong Today) do:

1.
2.
3.

Night 53 Reflections:

The GOOD: ____

____

____

The BAD: ____

____

____

My O2E: ____

____

____

TIME BLOCKS COMPLETED TODAY:

TE25	M60	T120

Potential Actions for Tomorrow:

1. ____
2. ____
3. ____

Reflections of the Day:

____

____

Are You D.O.N.E. Today? Yes No

DAILY ACTIONS: Week 8, Day 54

Personal Self Time:	TE25	M60	OT120
Social Self Time:	TE25	M60	OT120
Financial Self Time:	TE25	M60	OT120

Personal Self Goal for Day: TIME: _______

____

____

Social Self Goal for Day: TIME: _______

____

____

Financial Self Goal for Day: TIME: _______

____

____

Three Things I'm Grateful For:

1. ____
2. ____
3. ____

Did you hydrate today? YES NO

Three Things You M.U.S.T. (Make You Strong Today) do:

1. ____

____

2. ____

____

3. ____

Night 54 Reflections:

The GOOD: ____________________

____

____

The BAD: ____________________

____

____

My O2E: ____________________

____

____

TIME BLOCKS COMPLETED TODAY:

TE25	M60	T120

Potential Actions for Tomorrow:

1. ____________________
2. ____________________
3. ____________________

Reflections of the Day:

____

____

Are You D.O.N.E. Today? Yes No

DAILY ACTIONS: Week 8, Day 55

Personal Self Time:	TE25	M60	OT120
Social Self Time:	TE25	M60	OT120
Financial Self Time:	TE25	M60	OT120

Personal Self Goal for Day: TIME: _______

Social Self Goal for Day: TIME: _______

Financial Self Goal for Day: TIME: _______

Three Things I'm Grateful For:

1. ____________________
2. ____________________
3. ____________________

Did you hydrate today? YES NO

Three Things You M.U.S.T. (Make You Strong Today) do:

1. ____________________
2. ____________________
3. ____________________

Night 55 Reflections:

The GOOD: ____________________

____

____

The BAD: ____________________

____

____

My O2E: ____________________

____

____

TIME BLOCKS COMPLETED TODAY:

TE25	M60	T120

Potential Actions for Tomorrow:

1. ____________________
2. ____________________
3. ____________________

Reflections of the Day:

____

____

Are You D.O.N.E. Today? Yes No

DAILY ACTIONS: Week 8, Day 56

Personal Self Time:	TE25	M60	OT120
Social Self Time:	TE25	M60	OT120
Financial Self Time:	TE25	M60	OT120

Personal Self Goal for Day: TIME: _______

____

____

Social Self Goal for Day: TIME: _______

____

____

Financial Self Goal for Day: TIME: _______

____

____

Three Things I'm Grateful For:

1. ____
2. ____
3. ____

Did you hydrate today? YES NO

Three Things You M.U.S.T. (Make You Strong Today) do:

1. ____

____

2. ____

____

3. ____

Night 56 Reflections:

The GOOD: ______

______

______

The BAD: ______

______

______

My O2E: ______

______

______

TIME BLOCKS COMPLETED TODAY:

TE25	M60	T120

Potential Actions for Tomorrow:

1. ______
2. ______
3. ______

Reflections of the Day:

______

______

Are You D.O.N.E. Today? Yes No

WEEK 8 in Review

Personal Self for Week 1 Achieved? If not, why?

Social Self for Week 1 Achieved? If not, why?

Financial Self for Week 1 Achieved? If not, why?

TOTAL TIME BLOCKS FOR WEEK:

TE25	M60	T120

REVIEW YOUR <u>MONTHLY EXPECTATIONS</u> (MEs) TO MAKE SURE YOU ARE ON YOUR PATH FOR SUCCESS!!!

What is one thing I can do moving forward to better my week?

Thoughts for the Week:

MONTH 2 in Review

Personal MEs Achieved? If not, why?

Social MEs Achieved? If not, why?

Financial MEs Achieved? If not, why?

REVIEW YOUR MONTHLY EXPECTATIONS (MEs) TO MAKE SURE YOU ARE ON YOUR PATH FOR SUCCESS!!!

What is one thing I can do moving forward to better my month:

Monthly Reflection:

Month 2 is complete!

Congratulations to your progress and continuing to strive for your outcomes.

Let's get set for the beginning of Month 3.

Remember to reflect upon your "Monthly Expectations Sheet" and make sure you are on track for your Month 3 targets.

WEEK 9 Preview

Personal Self Outlook for Week: ______________________

____

____

Social Self Outlook for Week: ______________________

____

____

Financial Self Outlook for Week: ______________________

____

____

REVIEW YOUR MONTHLY EXPECTATIONS (MEs) TO MAKE SURE YOU ARE ON YOUR PATH FOR SUCCESS!!!

What time vampire will I slay this week?

____

Thoughts for the Week:

____

____

____

DAILY ACTIONS: Week 9, Day 57

Personal Self Time:	TE25	M60	OT120
Social Self Time:	TE25	M60	OT120
Financial Self Time:	TE25	M60	OT120

Personal Self Goal for Day: TIME: _______

____

____

Social Self Goal for Day: TIME: _______

____

____

Financial Self Goal for Day: TIME: _______

____

____

Three Things I'm Grateful For:

1. ____

2. ____

3. ____

Did you hydrate today? YES NO

Three Things You M.U.S.T. (Make You Strong Today) do:

1. ____

____

2. ____

____

3. ____

Night 57 Reflections:

The GOOD: ____________________

____

____

The BAD: ____________________

____

____

My O2E: ____________________

____

____

TIME BLOCKS COMPLETED TODAY:

TE25	M60	T120

Potential Actions for Tomorrow:

1. ____________________
2. ____________________
3. ____________________

Reflections of the Day:

____

____

Are You D.O.N.E. Today? Yes No

DAILY ACTIONS: Week 9, Day 58

Personal Self Time:	TE25	M60	OT120
Social Self Time:	TE25	M60	OT120
Financial Self Time:	TE25	M60	OT120

Personal Self Goal for Day: TIME: _______

____

____

Social Self Goal for Day: TIME: _______

____

____

Financial Self Goal for Day: TIME: _______

____

____

Three Things I'm Grateful For:

1. ____
2. ____
3. ____

Did you hydrate today? YES NO

Three Things You M.U.S.T. (Make You Strong Today) do:

1. ____

____

2. ____

____

3. ____

Night 58 Reflections:

The GOOD: ______________________________

____

____

The BAD: ______________________________

____

____

My O2E: ______________________________

____

____

TIME BLOCKS COMPLETED TODAY:

TE25	M60	T120

Potential Actions for Tomorrow:

1. ______________________________
2. ______________________________
3. ______________________________

Reflections of the Day:

____

____

Are You D.O.N.E. Today? Yes No

DAILY ACTIONS: Week 9, Day 59

Personal Self Time:	TE25	M60	OT120
Social Self Time:	TE25	M60	OT120
Financial Self Time:	TE25	M60	OT120

Personal Self Goal for Day: TIME: _______

____

____

Social Self Goal for Day: TIME: _______

____

____

Financial Self Goal for Day: TIME: _______

____

____

Three Things I'm Grateful For:

1. ____
2. ____
3. ____

Did you hydrate today? YES NO

Three Things You M.U.S.T. (Make You Strong Today) do:

1. ____

____

2. ____

____

3. ____

Night 59 Reflections:

The GOOD: ____________________

____

____

The BAD: ____________________

____

____

My O2E: ____________________

____

____

TIME BLOCKS COMPLETED TODAY:

TE25	M60	T120

Potential Actions for Tomorrow:

1. ____________________
2. ____________________
3. ____________________

Reflections of the Day:

____

____

Are You D.O.N.E. Today? Yes No

DAILY ACTIONS: Week 9, Day 60

Personal Self Time:	TE25	M60	OT120
Social Self Time:	TE25	M60	OT120
Financial Self Time:	TE25	M60	OT120

Personal Self Goal for Day: TIME: _______

____

____

Social Self Goal for Day: TIME: _______

____

____

Financial Self Goal for Day: TIME: _______

____

____

Three Things I'm Grateful For:

1. ____
2. ____
3. ____

Did you hydrate today? YES NO

Three Things You M.U.S.T. (Make You Strong Today) do:

1. ____

   ____
2. ____

   ____
3. ____

Night 60 Reflections:

The GOOD: ______________________________

____

____

The BAD: ______________________________

____

____

My O2E: ______________________________

____

____

TIME BLOCKS COMPLETED TODAY:

TE25	M60	T120

Potential Actions for Tomorrow:

1. ______________________________
2. ______________________________
3. ______________________________

Reflections of the Day:

____

____

Are You D.O.N.E. Today? Yes No

DAILY ACTIONS: Week 9, Day 61

Personal Self Time:	TE25	M60	OT120
Social Self Time:	TE25	M60	OT120
Financial Self Time:	TE25	M60	OT120

Personal Self Goal for Day: TIME: ______

____

____

Social Self Goal for Day: TIME: ______

____

____

Financial Self Goal for Day: TIME: ______

____

____

Three Things I'm Grateful For:

1. ______________________________
2. ______________________________
3. ______________________________

Did you hydrate today? YES NO

Three Things You M.U.S.T. (Make You Strong Today) do:

1. ______________________________

   ____
2. ______________________________

   ____
3. ______________________________

Night 61 Reflections:

The GOOD: ______________________________

____

____

The BAD: ______________________________

____

____

My O2E: ______________________________

____

____

TIME BLOCKS COMPLETED TODAY:

TE25	M60	T120

Potential Actions for Tomorrow:

1. ______________________________
2. ______________________________
3. ______________________________

Reflections of the Day:

____

____

Are You D.O.N.E. Today? Yes No

DAILY ACTIONS: Week 9, Day 62

Personal Self Time:	TE25	M60	OT120
Social Self Time:	TE25	M60	OT120
Financial Self Time:	TE25	M60	OT120

Personal Self Goal for Day: TIME: _______

____

____

Social Self Goal for Day: TIME: _______

____

____

Financial Self Goal for Day: TIME: _______

____

____

Three Things I'm Grateful For:

1. _______________
2. _______________
3. _______________

Did you hydrate today? YES NO

Three Things You M.U.S.T. (Make You Strong Today) do:

1. _______________

____

2. _______________

____

3. _______________

Night 62 Reflections:

The GOOD: ____________________

____

____

The BAD: ____________________

____

____

My O2E: ____________________

____

____

TIME BLOCKS COMPLETED TODAY:

TE25	M60	T120

Potential Actions for Tomorrow:

1. ____________________
2. ____________________
3. ____________________

Reflections of the Day:

____

____

Are You D.O.N.E. Today? Yes No

DAILY ACTIONS: Week 9, Day 63

Personal Self Time:	TE25	M60	OT120
Social Self Time:	TE25	M60	OT120
Financial Self Time:	TE25	M60	OT120

Personal Self Goal for Day: TIME: _______

____

____

Social Self Goal for Day: TIME: _______

____

____

Financial Self Goal for Day: TIME: _______

____

____

Three Things I'm Grateful For:

1. ____
2. ____
3. ____

Did you hydrate today? YES NO

Three Things You M.U.S.T. (Make You Strong Today) do:

1. ____

   ____
2. ____

   ____
3. ____

Night 63 Reflections:

The GOOD: ____________________

____

____

The BAD: ____________________

____

____

My O2E: ____________________

____

____

TIME BLOCKS COMPLETED TODAY:

TE25	M60	T120

Potential Actions for Tomorrow:

1. ____________________
2. ____________________
3. ____________________

Reflections of the Day:

____

____

Are You D.O.N.E. Today? Yes No

WEEK 9 in Review

Personal Self for Week 1 Achieved? If not, why?

Social Self for Week 1 Achieved? If not, why?

Financial Self for Week 1 Achieved? If not, why?

TOTAL TIME BLOCKS FOR WEEK:

TE25	M60	T120

REVIEW YOUR <u>MONTHLY EXPECTATIONS</u> (MEs) TO MAKE SURE YOU ARE ON YOUR PATH FOR SUCCESS!!!

What is one thing I can do moving forward to better my week?

Thoughts for the Week:

WEEK 10 Preview

Personal Self Outlook for Week: ______________________________

____

____

Social Self Outlook for Week: ______________________________

____

____

Financial Self Outlook for Week: ______________________________

____

____

REVIEW YOUR MONTHLY EXPECTATIONS (MEs) TO MAKE SURE YOU ARE ON YOUR PATH FOR SUCCESS!!!

What time vampire will I slay this week?

____

Thoughts for the Week:

____

____

____

DAILY ACTIONS: Week 10, Day 64

Personal Self Time:	TE25	M60	OT120
Social Self Time:	TE25	M60	OT120
Financial Self Time:	TE25	M60	OT120

Personal Self Goal for Day: TIME: ______

____

____

Social Self Goal for Day: TIME: ______

____

____

Financial Self Goal for Day: TIME: ______

____

____

Three Things I'm Grateful For:

1. ______________________________
2. ______________________________
3. ______________________________

Did you hydrate today? YES NO

Three Things You M.U.S.T. (Make You Strong Today) do:

1. ______________________________

   ____
2. ______________________________

   ____
3. ______________________________

Night 64 Reflections:

The GOOD: ______________________________

____

____

The BAD: ______________________________

____

____

My O2E: ______________________________

____

____

TIME BLOCKS COMPLETED TODAY:

TE25	M60	T120

Potential Actions for Tomorrow:

1. ______________________________
2. ______________________________
3. ______________________________

Reflections of the Day:

____

____

Are You D.O.N.E. Today? Yes No

DAILY ACTIONS: Week 10, Day 65

Personal Self Time:	TE25	M60	OT120
Social Self Time:	TE25	M60	OT120
Financial Self Time:	TE25	M60	OT120

Personal Self Goal for Day: TIME: _______

Social Self Goal for Day: TIME: _______

Financial Self Goal for Day: TIME: _______

Three Things I'm Grateful For:

1. ______
2. ______
3. ______

Did you hydrate today? YES NO

Three Things You M.U.S.T. (Make You Strong Today) do:

1. ______
2. ______
3. ______

Night 65 Reflections:

The GOOD: ____

____

____

The BAD: ____

____

____

My O2E: ____

____

____

TIME BLOCKS COMPLETED TODAY:

TE25	M60	T120

Potential Actions for Tomorrow:

1. ____
2. ____
3. ____

Reflections of the Day:

____

____

Are You D.O.N.E. Today? Yes No

DAILY ACTIONS: Week 10, Day 66

Personal Self Time:	TE25	M60	OT120
Social Self Time:	TE25	M60	OT120
Financial Self Time:	TE25	M60	OT120

Personal Self Goal for Day: TIME: _______

Social Self Goal for Day: TIME: _______

Financial Self Goal for Day: TIME: _______

Three Things I'm Grateful For:

1. ______
2. ______
3. ______

Did you hydrate today? YES NO

Three Things You M.U.S.T. (Make You Strong Today) do:

1. ______
2. ______
3. ______

Night 66 Reflections:

The GOOD: ____

____

____

The BAD: ____

____

____

My O2E: ____

____

____

TIME BLOCKS COMPLETED TODAY:

TE25	M60	T120

Potential Actions for Tomorrow:

1. ____
2. ____
3. ____

Reflections of the Day:

____

____

Are You D.O.N.E. Today? Yes No

DAILY ACTIONS: Week 10, Day 67

Personal Self Time:	TE25	M60	OT120
Social Self Time:	TE25	M60	OT120
Financial Self Time:	TE25	M60	OT120

Personal Self Goal for Day: TIME: ______

____

____

Social Self Goal for Day: TIME: ______

____

____

Financial Self Goal for Day: TIME: ______

____

____

Three Things I'm Grateful For:

1. ______________________________
2. ______________________________
3. ______________________________

Did you hydrate today? YES NO

Three Things You M.U.S.T. (Make You Strong Today) do:

1. ______________________________

   ____
2. ______________________________

   ____
3. ______________________________

Night 67 Reflections:

The GOOD: ______________________________

____

____

The BAD: ______________________________

____

____

My O2E: ______________________________

____

____

TIME BLOCKS COMPLETED TODAY:

TE25	M60	T120

Potential Actions for Tomorrow:

1. ______________________________
2. ______________________________
3. ______________________________

Reflections of the Day:

____

____

Are You D.O.N.E. Today? Yes No

DAILY ACTIONS: Week 10, Day 68

Personal Self Time:	TE25	M60	OT120
Social Self Time:	TE25	M60	OT120
Financial Self Time:	TE25	M60	OT120

Personal Self Goal for Day: TIME: _______

____

____

Social Self Goal for Day: TIME: _______

____

____

Financial Self Goal for Day: TIME: _______

____

____

Three Things I'm Grateful For:

1. ____
2. ____
3. ____

Did you hydrate today? YES NO

Three Things You M.U.S.T. (Make You Strong Today) do:

1. ____

   ____
2. ____

   ____
3. ____

Night 68 Reflections:

The GOOD: ____________________

____

____

The BAD: ____________________

____

____

My O2E: ____________________

____

____

TIME BLOCKS COMPLETED TODAY:

TE25	M60	T120

Potential Actions for Tomorrow:

1. ____________________
2. ____________________
3. ____________________

Reflections of the Day:

____

____

Are You D.O.N.E. Today? Yes No

DAILY ACTIONS: Week 10, Day 69

Personal Self Time:	TE25	M60	OT120
Social Self Time:	TE25	M60	OT120
Financial Self Time:	TE25	M60	OT120

Personal Self Goal for Day: TIME: _______

____

____

Social Self Goal for Day: TIME: _______

____

____

Financial Self Goal for Day: TIME: _______

____

____

Three Things I'm Grateful For:

1. ____
2. ____
3. ____

Did you hydrate today? YES NO

Three Things You M.U.S.T. (Make You Strong Today) do:

1. ____

   ____
2. ____

   ____
3. ____

Night 69 Reflections:

The GOOD: ______________________________

____

____

The BAD: ______________________________

____

____

My O2E: ______________________________

____

____

TIME BLOCKS COMPLETED TODAY:

TE25	M60	T120

Potential Actions for Tomorrow:

1. ______________________________
2. ______________________________
3. ______________________________

Reflections of the Day:

____

____

Are You D.O.N.E. Today? Yes No

DAILY ACTIONS: Week 10, Day 70

Personal Self Time:	TE25	M60	OT120
Social Self Time:	TE25	M60	OT120
Financial Self Time:	TE25	M60	OT120

Personal Self Goal for Day: TIME: ______

____

____

Social Self Goal for Day: TIME: ______

____

____

Financial Self Goal for Day: TIME: ______

____

____

Three Things I'm Grateful For:

1. ______________________________
2. ______________________________
3. ______________________________

Did you hydrate today? YES NO

Three Things You M.U.S.T. (Make You Strong Today) do:

1. ______________________________

____

2. ______________________________

____

3. ______________________________

Night 70 Reflections:

The GOOD: ______________________________

____

____

The BAD: ______________________________

____

____

My O2E: ______________________________

____

____

TIME BLOCKS COMPLETED TODAY:

TE25	M60	T120

Potential Actions for Tomorrow:

1. ______________________________
2. ______________________________
3. ______________________________

Reflections of the Day:

____

____

Are You D.O.N.E. Today? Yes No

WEEK 10 in Review

Personal Self for Week 1 Achieved? If not, why?

Social Self for Week 1 Achieved? If not, why?

Financial Self for Week 1 Achieved? If not, why?

TOTAL TIME BLOCKS FOR WEEK:

TE25	M60	T120

REVIEW YOUR MONTHLY EXPECTATIONS (MEs) TO MAKE SURE YOU ARE ON YOUR PATH FOR SUCCESS!!!

What is one thing I can do moving forward to better my week?

Thoughts for the Week:

WEEK 11 Preview

Personal Self Outlook for Week: ______________________

____

____

Social Self Outlook for Week: ______________________

____

____

Financial Self Outlook for Week: ______________________

____

____

REVIEW YOUR MONTHLY EXPECTATIONS (MEs) TO MAKE SURE YOU ARE ON YOUR PATH FOR SUCCESS!!!

What time vampire will I slay this week?

____

Thoughts for the week:

____

____

____

DAILY ACTIONS: Week 11, Day 71

Personal Self Time:	TE25	M60	OT120
Social Self Time:	TE25	M60	OT120
Financial Self Time:	TE25	M60	OT120

Personal Self Goal for Day: TIME: _______

____

____

Social Self Goal for Day: TIME: _______

____

____

Financial Self Goal for Day: TIME: _______

____

____

Three Things I'm Grateful For:

1. ____
2. ____
3. ____

Did you hydrate today? YES NO

Three Things You M.U.S.T. (Make You Strong Today) do:

1. ____

   ____
2. ____

   ____
3. ____

Night 71 Reflections:

The GOOD: ____

____

____

The BAD: ____

____

____

My O2E: ____

____

____

TIME BLOCKS COMPLETED TODAY:

TE25	M60	T120

Potential Actions for Tomorrow:

1. ____
2. ____
3. ____

Reflections of the Day:

____

____

Are You D.O.N.E. Today? Yes No

DAILY ACTIONS: Week 11, Day 72

Personal Self Time:	TE25	M60	OT120
Social Self Time:	TE25	M60	OT120
Financial Self Time:	TE25	M60	OT120

Personal Self Goal for Day: TIME: _______

____

____

Social Self Goal for Day: TIME: _______

____

____

Financial Self Goal for Day: TIME: _______

____

____

Three Things I'm Grateful For:

1. ____
2. ____
3. ____

Did you hydrate today? YES NO

Three Things You M.U.S.T. (Make You Strong Today) do:

1. ____

   ____
2. ____

   ____
3. ____

Night 72 Reflections:

The GOOD: ____

____

____

The BAD: ____

____

____

My O2E: ____

____

____

TIME BLOCKS COMPLETED TODAY:

TE25	M60	T120

Potential Actions for Tomorrow:

1. ____
2. ____
3. ____

Reflections of the Day:

____

____

Are You D.O.N.E. Today? Yes No

DAILY ACTIONS: Week 11, Day 73

Personal Self Time:	TE25	M60	OT120
Social Self Time:	TE25	M60	OT120
Financial Self Time:	TE25	M60	OT120

Personal Self Goal for Day: TIME: ______

______

______

Social Self Goal for Day: TIME: ______

______

______

Financial Self Goal for Day: TIME: ______

______

______

Three Things I'm Grateful For:

1. ______
2. ______
3. ______

Did you hydrate today? YES NO

Three Things You M.U.S.T. (Make You Strong Today) do:

1. ______

______

2. ______

______

3. ______

Night 73 Reflections:

The GOOD: ____

The BAD: ____

My O2E: ____

TIME BLOCKS COMPLETED TODAY:

TE25	M60	T120

Potential Actions for Tomorrow:

1. ____
2. ____
3. ____

Reflections of the Day:

Are You D.O.N.E. Today? Yes No

DAILY ACTIONS: Week 11, Day 74

Personal Self Time:	TE25	M60	OT120
Social Self Time:	TE25	M60	OT120
Financial Self Time:	TE25	M60	OT120

Personal Self Goal for Day: TIME: ______

____

____

Social Self Goal for Day: TIME: ______

____

____

Financial Self Goal for Day: TIME: ______

____

____

Three Things I'm Grateful For:

1. ______________________________
2. ______________________________
3. ______________________________

Did you hydrate today? YES NO

Three Things You M.U.S.T. (Make You Strong Today) do:

1. ______________________________

____

2. ______________________________

____

3. ______________________________

Night 74 Reflections:

The GOOD: ____________________

____

____

The BAD: ____________________

____

____

My O2E: ____________________

____

____

TIME BLOCKS COMPLETED TODAY:

TE25	M60	T120

Potential Actions for Tomorrow:

1. ____________________
2. ____________________
3. ____________________

Reflections of the Day:

____

____

Are You D.O.N.E. Today? Yes No

DAILY ACTIONS: Week 11, Day 75

Personal Self Time:	TE25	M60	OT120
Social Self Time:	TE25	M60	OT120
Financial Self Time:	TE25	M60	OT120

Personal Self Goal for Day: TIME: _______

____

____

Social Self Goal for Day: TIME: _______

____

____

Financial Self Goal for Day: TIME: _______

____

____

Three Things I'm Grateful For:

1. ______________________________
2. ______________________________
3. ______________________________

Did you hydrate today? YES NO

Three Things You M.U.S.T. (Make You Strong Today) do:

1. ______________________________

   ____
2. ______________________________

   ____
3. ______________________________

Night 75 Reflections:

The GOOD: ______________________________

____

____

The BAD: ______________________________

____

____

My O2E: ______________________________

____

____

TIME BLOCKS COMPLETED TODAY:

TE25	M60	T120

Potential Actions for Tomorrow:

1. ______________________________
2. ______________________________
3. ______________________________

Reflections of the Day:

____

____

Are You D.O.N.E. Today? Yes No

DAILY ACTIONS: Week 11, Day 76

Personal Self Time:	TE25	M60	OT120
Social Self Time:	TE25	M60	OT120
Financial Self Time:	TE25	M60	OT120

Personal Self Goal for Day: TIME: ______

______

______

Social Self Goal for Day: TIME: ______

______

______

Financial Self Goal for Day: TIME: ______

______

______

Three Things I'm Grateful For:

1. ______
2. ______
3. ______

Did you hydrate today? YES NO

Three Things You M.U.S.T. (Make You Strong Today) do:

1. ______

   ______
2. ______

   ______
3. ______

Night 76 Reflections:

The GOOD: ______________________________

____

____

The BAD: ______________________________

____

____

My O2E: ______________________________

____

____

TIME BLOCKS COMPLETED TODAY:

TE25	M60	T120

Potential Actions for Tomorrow:

1. ______________________________
2. ______________________________
3. ______________________________

Reflections of the Day:

____

____

Are You D.O.N.E. Today? Yes No

DAILY ACTIONS: Week 11, Day 77

Personal Self Time:	TE25	M60	OT120
Social Self Time:	TE25	M60	OT120
Financial Self Time:	TE25	M60	OT120

Personal Self Goal for Day: TIME: _______

Social Self Goal for Day: TIME: _______

Financial Self Goal for Day: TIME: _______

Three Things I'm Grateful For:

1. ____
2. ____
3. ____

Did you hydrate today? YES NO

Three Things You M.U.S.T. (Make You Strong Today) do:

1. ____
2. ____
3. ____

Night 77 Reflections:

The GOOD: ______________________________

____

____

The BAD: ______________________________

____

____

My O2E: ______________________________

____

____

TIME BLOCKS COMPLETED TODAY:

TE25	M60	T120

Potential Actions for Tomorrow:

1. ______________________________
2. ______________________________
3. ______________________________

Reflections of the Day:

____

____

Are You D.O.N.E. Today? Yes No

WEEK 11 in Review

Personal Self for Week 1 Achieved? If not, why?

____

Social Self for Week 1 Achieved? If not, why?

____

Financial Self for Week 1 Achieved? If not, why?

____

TOTAL TIME BLOCKS FOR WEEK:

TE25	M60	T120

REVIEW YOUR MONTHLY EXPECTATIONS (MEs) TO MAKE SURE YOU ARE ON YOUR PATH FOR SUCCESS!!!

What is one thing I can do moving forward to better my week?

____

Thoughts for the Week:

____

____

____

____

____

WEEK 12 Preview

Personal Self Outlook for Week: ______________________________

____

____

Social Self Outlook for Week: ________________________________

____

____

Financial Self Outlook for Week: _____________________________

____

____

REVIEW YOUR MONTHLY EXPECTATIONS (MEs) TO MAKE SURE YOU ARE ON YOUR PATH FOR SUCCESS!!!

What time vampire will I slay this week?

____

Thoughts for the Week:

____

____

____

DAILY ACTIONS: Week 12, Day 78

Personal Self Time:	TE25	M60	OT120
Social Self Time:	TE25	M60	OT120
Financial Self Time:	TE25	M60	OT120

Personal Self Goal for Day: TIME: _______

____

____

Social Self Goal for Day: TIME: _______

____

____

Financial Self Goal for Day: TIME: _______

____

____

Three Things I'm Grateful For:

1. ____
2. ____
3. ____

Did you hydrate today? YES NO

Three Things You M.U.S.T. (Make You Strong Today) do:

1. ____

   ____
2. ____

   ____
3. ____

Night 78 Reflections:

The GOOD: ____________________

____

____

The BAD: ____________________

____

____

My O2E: ____________________

____

____

TIME BLOCKS COMPLETED TODAY:

TE25	M60	T120

Potential Actions for Tomorrow:

1. ____________________
2. ____________________
3. ____________________

Reflections of the Day:

____

____

Are You D.O.N.E. Today? Yes No

DAILY ACTIONS: Week 12, Day 79

Personal Self Time:	TE25	M60	OT120
Social Self Time:	TE25	M60	OT120
Financial Self Time:	TE25	M60	OT120

Personal Self Goal for Day: TIME: _______

____

____

Social Self Goal for Day: TIME: _______

____

____

Financial Self Goal for Day: TIME: _______

____

____

Three Things I'm Grateful For:

1. ____
2. ____
3. ____

Did you hydrate today? YES NO

Three Things You M.U.S.T. (Make You Strong Today) do:

1. ____

   ____
2. ____

   ____
3. ____

Night 79 Reflections:

The GOOD: ____________________

____

____

The BAD: ____________________

____

____

My O2E: ____________________

____

____

TIME BLOCKS COMPLETED TODAY:

TE25	M60	T120

Potential Actions for Tomorrow:

1. ____________________
2. ____________________
3. ____________________

Reflections of the Day:

____

____

Are You D.O.N.E. Today? Yes No

DAILY ACTIONS: Week 12, Day 80

Personal Self Time:	TE25	M60	OT120
Social Self Time:	TE25	M60	OT120
Financial Self Time:	TE25	M60	OT120

Personal Self Goal for Day: TIME: ______

______

______

Social Self Goal for Day: TIME: ______

______

______

Financial Self Goal for Day: TIME: ______

______

______

Three Things I'm Grateful For:

1. ______
2. ______
3. ______

Did you hydrate today? YES NO

Three Things You M.U.S.T. (Make You Strong Today) do:

1. ______

   ______
2. ______

   ______
3. ______

Night 80 Reflections:

The GOOD: ____

____

____

The BAD: ____

____

____

My O2E: ____

____

____

TIME BLOCKS COMPLETED TODAY:

TE25	M60	T120

Potential Actions for Tomorrow:

1. ____
2. ____
3. ____

Reflections of the Day:

____

____

Are You D.O.N.E. Today? Yes No

DAILY ACTIONS: Week 12, Day 81

Personal Self Time:	TE25	M60	OT120
Social Self Time:	TE25	M60	OT120
Financial Self Time:	TE25	M60	OT120

Personal Self Goal for Day: TIME: _______

____

____

Social Self Goal for Day: TIME: _______

____

____

Financial Self Goal for Day: TIME: _______

____

____

Three Things I'm Grateful For:

1. _______________
2. _______________
3. _______________

Did you hydrate today? YES NO

Three Things You M.U.S.T. (Make You Strong Today) do:

1. _______________

   ____
2. _______________

   ____
3. _______________

Night 81 Reflections:

The GOOD: ______________________________

____

____

The BAD: ______________________________

____

____

My O2E: ______________________________

____

____

TIME BLOCKS COMPLETED TODAY:

TE25	M60	T120

Potential Actions for Tomorrow:

1. ______________________________
2. ______________________________
3. ______________________________

Reflections of the Day:

____

____

Are You D.O.N.E. Today? Yes No

DAILY ACTIONS: Week 12, Day 82

Personal Self Time:	TE25	M60	OT120
Social Self Time:	TE25	M60	OT120
Financial Self Time:	TE25	M60	OT120

Personal Self Goal for Day: TIME: _______

____

____

Social Self Goal for Day: TIME: _______

____

____

Financial Self Goal for Day: TIME: _______

____

____

Three Things I'm Grateful For:

1. ____
2. ____
3. ____

Did you hydrate today? YES NO

Three Things You M.U.S.T. (Make You Strong Today) do:

1. ____

   ____
2. ____

   ____
3. ____

Night 82 Reflections:

The GOOD: ____

____

____

The BAD: ____

____

____

My O2E: ____

____

____

TIME BLOCKS COMPLETED TODAY:

TE25	M60	T120

Potential Actions for Tomorrow:

1. ____
2. ____
3. ____

Reflections of the Day:

____

____

Are You D.O.N.E. Today? Yes No

DAILY ACTIONS: Week 12, Day 83

Personal Self Time:	TE25	M60	OT120
Social Self Time:	TE25	M60	OT120
Financial Self Time:	TE25	M60	OT120

Personal Self Goal for Day: TIME: _______

Social Self Goal for Day: TIME: _______

Financial Self Goal for Day: TIME: _______

Three Things I'm Grateful For:

1. ____________________
2. ____________________
3. ____________________

Did you hydrate today? YES NO

Three Things You M.U.S.T. (Make You Strong Today) do:

1. ____________________
2. ____________________
3. ____________________

Night 83 Reflections:

The GOOD: ____________________

____

____

The BAD: ____________________

____

____

My O2E: ____________________

____

____

TIME BLOCKS COMPLETED TODAY:

TE25	M60	T120

Potential Actions for Tomorrow:

1. ____________________
2. ____________________
3. ____________________

Reflections of the Day:

____

____

Are You D.O.N.E. Today? Yes No

DAILY ACTIONS: Week 12, Day 84

Personal Self Time:	TE25	M60	OT120
Social Self Time:	TE25	M60	OT120
Financial Self Time:	TE25	M60	OT120

Personal Self Goal for Day: TIME: _______

____

____

Social Self Goal for Day: TIME: _______

____

____

Financial Self Goal for Day: TIME: _______

____

____

Three Things I'm Grateful For:

1. ______________________________
2. ______________________________
3. ______________________________

Did you hydrate today? YES NO

Three Things You M.U.S.T. (Make You Strong Today) do:

1. ______________________________

____

2. ______________________________

____

3. ______________________________

Night 84 Reflections:

The GOOD: ______________________________

____

____

The BAD: ______________________________

____

____

My O2E: ______________________________

____

____

TIME BLOCKS COMPLETED TODAY:

TE25	M60	T120

Potential Actions for Tomorrow:

1. ______________________________
2. ______________________________
3. ______________________________

Reflections of the Day:

____

____

Are You D.O.N.E. Today? Yes No

WEEK 12 in Review

Personal Self for Week 1 Achieved? If not, why?

Social Self for Week 1 Achieved? If not, why?

Financial Self for Week 1 Achieved? If not, why?

TOTAL TIME BLOCKS FOR WEEK:

TE25	M60	T120

REVIEW YOUR MONTHLY EXPECTATIONS (MEs) TO MAKE SURE YOU ARE ON YOUR PATH FOR SUCCESS!!!

What is one thing I can do moving forward to better my week?

Thoughts for the Week:

MONTH 3 in Review

Personal MEs Achieved? If not, why?

Social MEs Achieved? If not, why?

Financial MEs Achieved? If not, why?

REVIEW YOUR MONTHLY EXPECTATIONS (MEs) TO MAKE SURE YOU ARE ON YOUR PATH FOR SUCCESS!!!

What is one thing I can do moving forward to better my month:

Monthly Reflection:

Month 3 is complete!

Congratulations to your progress and continuing to strive for your outcomes.

One Week Left!

Time to finish strong!

Remember to reflect upon your “Monthly Expectations Sheet” and make sure you are on track for your Month 3 targets.

WEEK 13 Preview

Personal Self Outlook for Week: ________________________________

____

____

Social Self Outlook for Week: ________________________________

____

____

Financial Self Outlook for Week: ________________________________

____

____

REVIEW YOUR MONTHLY EXPECTATIONS (MEs) TO MAKE SURE YOU ARE ON YOUR PATH FOR SUCCESS!!!

What time vampire will I slay this week?

____

Thoughts for the Week:

____

____

____

DAILY ACTIONS: Week 13, Day 85

Personal Self Time:	TE25	M60	OT120
Social Self Time:	TE25	M60	OT120
Financial Self Time:	TE25	M60	OT120

Personal Self Goal for Day: TIME: _______

____

____

Social Self Goal for Day: TIME: _______

____

____

Financial Self Goal for Day: TIME: _______

____

____

Three Things I'm Grateful For:

1. ____
2. ____
3. ____

Did you hydrate today? YES NO

Three Things You M.U.S.T. (Make You Strong Today) do:

1. ____

   ____
2. ____

   ____
3. ____

Night 85 Reflections:

The GOOD: ______________________________

____

____

The BAD: ______________________________

____

____

My O2E: ______________________________

____

____

TIME BLOCKS COMPLETED TODAY:

TE25	M60	T120

Potential Actions for Tomorrow:

1. ______________________________
2. ______________________________
3. ______________________________

Reflections of the Day:

____

____

Are You D.O.N.E. Today? Yes No

DAILY ACTIONS: Week 13, Day 86

Personal Self Time:	TE25	M60	OT120
Social Self Time:	TE25	M60	OT120
Financial Self Time:	TE25	M60	OT120

Personal Self Goal for Day: TIME: _______

____

____

Social Self Goal for Day: TIME: _______

____

____

Financial Self Goal for Day: TIME: _______

____

____

Three Things I'm Grateful For:

1. _______________
2. _______________
3. _______________

Did you hydrate today? YES NO

Three Things You M.U.S.T. (Make You Strong Today) do:

1. _______________

   ____
2. _______________

   ____
3. _______________

Night 86 Reflections:

The GOOD: ____

____

____

The BAD: ____

____

____

My O2E: ____

____

____

TIME BLOCKS COMPLETED TODAY:

TE25	M60	T120

Potential Actions for Tomorrow:

1. ____
2. ____
3. ____

Reflections of the Day:

____

____

Are You D.O.N.E. Today? Yes No

DAILY ACTIONS: Week 13, Day 87

Personal Self Time:	TE25	M60	OT120
Social Self Time:	TE25	M60	OT120
Financial Self Time:	TE25	M60	OT120

Personal Self Goal for Day: TIME: _______

____

____

Social Self Goal for Day: TIME: _______

____

____

Financial Self Goal for Day: TIME: _______

____

____

Three Things I'm Grateful For:

1. ______________________________
2. ______________________________
3. ______________________________

Did you hydrate today? YES NO

Three Things You M.U.S.T. (Make You Strong Today) do:

1. ______________________________

____

2. ______________________________

____

3. ______________________________

Night 87 Reflections:

The GOOD: ____________________

____

____

The BAD: ____________________

____

____

My O2E: ____________________

____

____

TIME BLOCKS COMPLETED TODAY:

TE25	M60	T120

Potential Actions for Tomorrow:

1. ____________________
2. ____________________
3. ____________________

Reflections of the Day:

____

____

Are You D.O.N.E. Today? Yes No

DAILY ACTIONS: Week 13, Day 88

Personal Self Time:	TE25	M60	OT120
Social Self Time:	TE25	M60	OT120
Financial Self Time:	TE25	M60	OT120

Personal Self Goal for Day: TIME: ______

______

______

Social Self Goal for Day: TIME: ______

______

______

Financial Self Goal for Day: TIME: ______

______

______

Three Things I'm Grateful For:

1. ______
2. ______
3. ______

Did you hydrate today? YES NO

Three Things You M.U.S.T. (Make You Strong Today) do:

1. ______

   ______
2. ______

   ______
3. ______

Night 88 Reflections:

The GOOD: ____

____

____

The BAD: ____

____

____

My O2E: ____

____

____

TIME BLOCKS COMPLETED TODAY:

TE25	M60	T120

Potential Actions for Tomorrow:

1. ____
2. ____
3. ____

Reflections of the Day:

____

____

Are You D.O.N.E. Today? Yes No

DAILY ACTIONS: Week 13, Day 89

Personal Self Time:	TE25	M60	OT120
Social Self Time:	TE25	M60	OT120
Financial Self Time:	TE25	M60	OT120

Personal Self Goal for Day: TIME: _______

____

____

Social Self Goal for Day: TIME: _______

____

____

Financial Self Goal for Day: TIME: _______

____

____

Three Things I'm Grateful For:

1. ____
2. ____
3. ____

Did you hydrate today? YES NO

Three Things You M.U.S.T. (Make You Strong Today) do:

1. ____
   ____
2. ____
   ____
3. ____

Night 89 Reflections:

The GOOD: ______________________________

____

____

The BAD: ______________________________

____

____

My O2E: ______________________________

____

____

TIME BLOCKS COMPLETED TODAY:

TE25	M60	T120

Potential Actions for Tomorrow:

1. ______________________________
2. ______________________________
3. ______________________________

Reflections of the Day:

____

____

Are You D.O.N.E. Today? Yes No

DAILY ACTIONS: Week 13, Day 90

Personal Self Time:	TE25	M60	OT120
Social Self Time:	TE25	M60	OT120
Financial Self Time:	TE25	M60	OT120

Personal Self Goal for Day: TIME: _______

____

____

Social Self Goal for Day: TIME: _______

____

____

Financial Self Goal for Day: TIME: _______

____

____

Three Things I'm Grateful For:

1. ____
2. ____
3. ____

Did you hydrate today? YES NO

Three Things You M.U.S.T. (Make You Strong Today) do:

1. ____

   ____
2. ____

   ____
3. ____

Night 90 Reflections:

The GOOD: ______________________________

____

____

The BAD: ______________________________

____

____

My O2E: ______________________________

____

____

TIME BLOCKS COMPLETED TODAY:

TE25	M60	T120

Potential Actions for Tomorrow:

1. ______________________________
2. ______________________________
3. ______________________________

Reflections of the Day:

____

____

Are You D.O.N.E. Today? Yes No

DAILY ACTIONS: Week 13, Day 91

Personal Self Time:	TE25	M60	OT120
Social Self Time:	TE25	M60	OT120
Financial Self Time:	TE25	M60	OT120

Personal Self Goal for Day: TIME: _______

____

____

Social Self Goal for Day: TIME: _______

____

____

Financial Self Goal for Day: TIME: _______

____

____

Three Things I'm Grateful For:

1. ______________________________
2. ______________________________
3. ______________________________

Did you hydrate today? YES NO

Three Things You M.U.S.T. (Make You Strong Today) do:

1. ______________________________

   ____
2. ______________________________

   ____
3. ______________________________

Night 91 Reflections:

The GOOD: ______________________________

____

____

The BAD: ______________________________

____

____

My O2E: ______________________________

____

____

TIME BLOCKS COMPLETED TODAY:

TE25	M60	T120

Potential Actions for Tomorrow:

1. ______________________________
2. ______________________________
3. ______________________________

Reflections of the Day:

____

____

Are You D.O.N.E. Today? Yes No

WEEK 13 in Review

Personal Self for Week 1 Achieved? If not, why?

____

Social Self for Week 1 Achieved? If not, why?

____

Financial Self for Week 1 Achieved? If not, why?

____

TOTAL TIME BLOCKS FOR WEEK:

TE25	M60	T120

REVIEW YOUR MONTHLY EXPECTATIONS (MEs) TO MAKE SURE YOU ARE ON YOUR PATH FOR SUCCESS!!!

What is one thing I can do moving forward to better my week?

____

Thoughts for the Week:

____

____

____

____

____

MONTH 3 in Review (one more time!) a.k.a. Your 90-Day Goals

90-Day Personal Goals Achieved? If not, why?

90-Day Social Goals Achieved? If not, why?

90-Day Financial Goals Achieved? If not, why?

90 Day Goals Reflections and final thoughts on your journey:

FINAL THOUGHTS

Congratulations on getting though your 90-day journey!

You have made amazing strides during these 13 weeks and I encourage you to keep the momentum going.

If you desire to take your progress to the next level, reach out to me at terence@terenceyoungmd.com and I would be happy to chat with you. Let's see how I can best support you.

Again, congratulations on the hard work and check out the resources that I have available at:

www.terenceyoungmd.com

For all the books and supplemental products, you can check out:

www.docdeliversbooks.com

Take care and be well!

Terence Young, M.D.

Made in the USA
San Bernardino, CA
08 January 2019